UNUSUAL & UNIQUE OVERNIGHT

directory

CONTENTS

caves, igloos, treehouses, planes, trains, cars, helicopters, boats, underground, underwater, designer, kids, huts, cabins, churches, historic, a giant dog, a boat, islands, lighthouses, desert tents, palaces, castles, ice hotels, prisons, eco resorts, views, theme, bling, romantic, revolving, cranes, towers...

...sleep somewhere with a story to share.

For a life less ordinary

Our Manifesto

We believe in the courage to stand apart, to seek the road less travelled.

The audacity to make a difference. Curiosity to question why, boldness to question why not.

A thirst for adventure and a passion to stamp our name on a life well lived.

Along the way, we met you. Friends with a lust for exceptional experiences, Unusual and Unique places to stay. Those who realise the difference between being a traveller and a tourist.

Every GoUnusual property has a story. Some are obvious, some are not. But each has stirred us enough to demand that it be shared. And in sharing, we hand the story over to you. Where will you take it?

It's not about the time.

It's not about the money.

It's about how we choose to live our life. *A life less ordinary.*

WELCOME

Our overnight mantra of 'Sleep with a Story' has become a rallying call to a wide audience of travellers dissatisfied with bland hotels for their increasingly precious holidays. People thought we were joking when we wrote about sleeping in train carriages, igloos and giant dogs back in 2004. Yet this quiet revolution towards 'experiential hotels' has gathered pace since Simon, Sid and I set out our first efforts online with a handful of hotels.

Increasingly, our blogs and event calendars - read by 150,000 people last year - are guiding the decisions of readers to favourite cites, off the beaten path locations, activities, bars and, places to eat. Your feedback and support is invaluable for us to identify new places to review and destinations to feature.

A million people every year visit our websites and we now list over 300 properties around the world. Links are detailed in each entry should you want to review their prices, latest news or make a booking online. Following your interest in social media, we now have thousands of comments to help us rank favourites in the guide.

This directory celebrates Unusual and Unique places to stay. It has been an amazing journey for the team and I to collate these entries. I hope you enjoy our selection and that it provides inspiration 'for a life less ordinary'.

Steve Dobson
January 2013

Steve@uhotw.com

UNUSUAL AND UNIQUE HOTELS AROUND THE WORLD

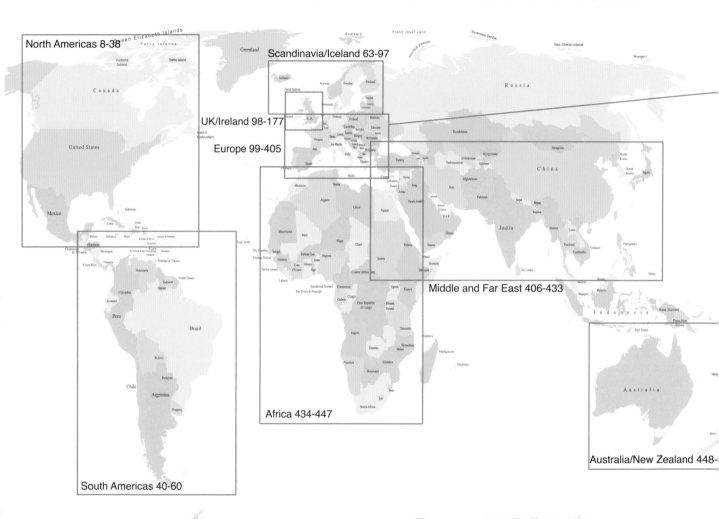

North Americas 8-38

Scandinavia/Iceland 63-97

UK/Ireland 98-177

Europe 99-405

Middle and Far East 406-433

Africa 434-447

South Americas 40-60

Australia/New Zealand 448-

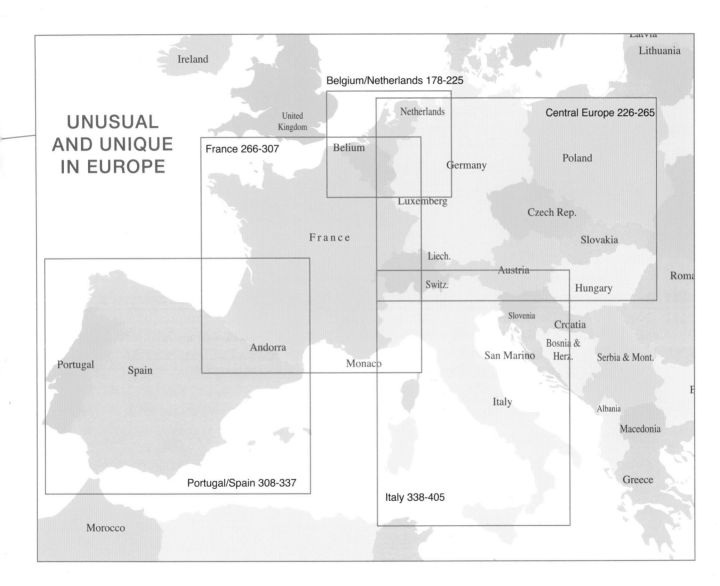

North America
USA, Canada, Mexico

Key

Entries in **Bold** typeface indicate full page entries with a photo.
Others are additional indexed entries.

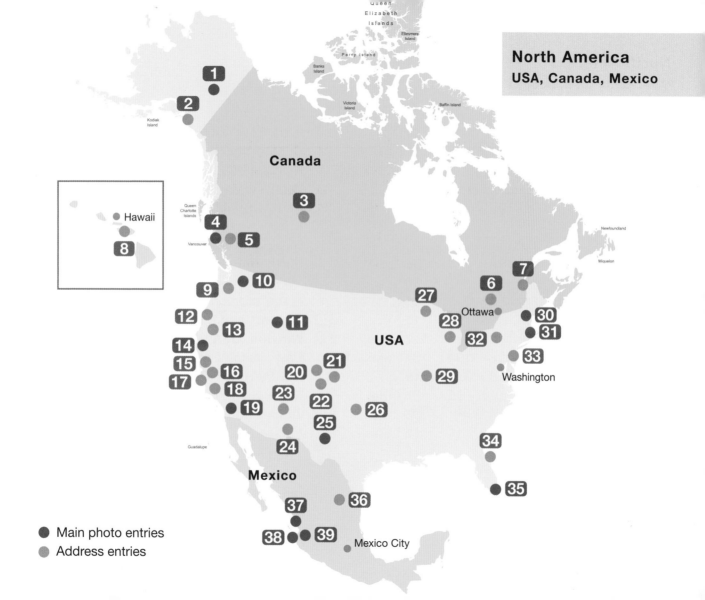

North America
USA, Canada, Mexico

Canada

USA

Ottawa

Washington

Mexico

Mexico City

Hawaii

● Main photo entries
● Address entries

Queen
Elizabeth
Islands

Ellesmere
Island

Parry Island

Banks
Island

Victoria
Island

Baffin Island

Newfoundland

Miquelon

Kodiak
Island

Queen
Charlotte
Islands

Vancouver

Guadalupe

AURORA EXPRESS

RAILROAD CARS MANHANDLED UP A MOUNTAIN FOR A BETTER VIEW

The Aurora Express, only 20 minutes from Fairbanks International Airport, offers lodging in historic railroad cars that have been transported halfway up a mountain to give a better view of Fairbanks and the Tanana valley far below.

Susan Wilson originally purchased the caboose as a present for husband Mike, who refused to let the challenge of moving a 41 feet long, 52,000 pound caboose halfway up a mountain defeat him. After the caboose, two 1956 Pullman Company railcars - originally used on the Alaska Railroad - were purchased and again Mike would not let the challenges of their relocation defeat his ingenuity. 85 ft long, 10 ft wide and each weighing 90 tons, these Pullman railcars provided an engineering challenge to deliver through the hairpin curves and narrow passes of Fairbanks.

Now fully restored, the Aurora Express consists of seven authentic Alaska Railroad car suites, resting on winding track.

Some of the suites are for couples with a ----queen size bed, private bath - and most enjoyable of all, lounge chairs where you can sit in comfort in the covered observation deck.

Other suites offer multiple occupancy, such as the 1956 Pullman private sleeper car that has two baths and can accommodate from one to four people. The 'Arlene' has been renovated into a private 85-foot car with 2 bedrooms suitable for families.

LOCATION AND ACTIVITIES

While Fairbanks displays President Harding's Railroad Car, "Denali" at Pioneer Park, you might also want to see the historic log cabins brought together from all over Alaska to create a historic gold rush town, with information on each of the dwellings.

"Best views from impossible railroad in the sky"

The Aurora Express
P.O. Box 80128
Fairbanks, AK 99708
United States of America
www.GoUnusual.com/AuroraExpress

• Bed & Breakfast

FREE SPIRIT SPHERES
SPHERICAL TREEHOUSES

Eve, Eryn and Melody are three spherical treehouses, suspended in a patch of Vancouver Island forest. Even the smallest, single-person-sized Eve, provides a spiritual connection for guests to the forest. These spheres sway in time with the trees and guests comment on how they encourage creative thought. Eryn is the largest wooden sphere (Melody is fibreglass built) and sleeps 2 comfortably, with a third person in a loft bed.

The motion in a sphere is a slow, gentle rocking when the wind blows. The rope tethers are almost vertical, which lets the treetops move considerably while hardly moving the sphere at all. The sphere movement is a muted average of the movement of the three treetops.

Beautifully crafted, the joinery is yacht-style with brass trim, varnished wood and cane doors. The treehouses have closets on either side of the door. These function as partial bulkheads to reinforce the door opening as well as adding cupboard space. A shared composting toilet outhouse is located at the base of the spheres. More traditional facilities are found 60 metres from the spheres and include: 2 washrooms, 2 showers, a sauna and a covered deck with barbecue and picnicking resources. Bedding and towels are supplied.

Each sphere is wired for power and has built in speakers for those who wish to bring their own music... the perfect opportunity to experience true surround sound.

Longer rentals are offered as well as the opportunity to purchase a pre-built sphere of your own.

LOCATION AND ACTIVITIES

Free Spirit Spheres is approximately 30km north of Parksville on Vancouver Island along the Inland Island Hwy (#19), near Qualicum Bay. The acreage is close to Horne Lake Caves, Georgia Strait and Mount Washington.

There are a wide variety of restaurants and eateries within 5 to 25 kms of the rental spheres.

"To enable people to move into and inhabit the forest without taking it down first. To live in and among the trees and to use them for a foundation"

Free Spirit Spheres
420 Horne Lake Road
Qualicum Beach BC
V9K 1Z7
Canada
www.GoUnusual.com/FreeSpiritSpheres

• Vacation rental

ROLLING HUTS
DESIGNER CAMPING UNDER THE STARS

Rolling Huts, located in Washington's Methow Valley, are designed as a modern alternative to camping by Tom Kundig of Olson Kundig Architects in Seattle. The six huts are grouped as a herd, each with views of the mountains.

Each hut comes equipped with a small refrigerator, microwave and Wi-Fi as well as a working fireplace to keep you warm. There is a sleeping platform perfect for two, and modular furniture in the living area that can be reconfigured to sleep two more. Huts have an adjacent portable toilet and full bathrooms and showers are housed in the centrally located barn a short distance away.

Although the Rolling Huts are luxurious, you need to remember that facilities provided are more like camping than a hotel. You'll need to bring your own sleeping bag or blankets - although sheets, pillow cases and towels are provided. The huts have a microwave but don't include a stove. There is a communal gas barbecue, as well as some wood/charcoal units, but you'll need to stock up on charcoal and bring utensils.

Importantly, huts are equipped with the likely most essential morning item - an electric kettle and coffee maker!

There is a water faucet outside of each hut.

LOCATION AND ACTIVITIES

Located in the North Cascades, the Methow Valley is a scenic destination with beautiful mountain vistas, forests and wildflowers. With warm, dry summers and snowy winters, the valley offers a variety of outdoor adventures for all ages and skill levels. Depending on route it's about 230 miles form Seattle, however the most popular and scenic route to Eastern Washington is closed during the winter mid-November through mid- April.

Please check the Mountain Pass Road Information Reports during this time to verify your route.

"Standing like cattle on a ranch"

Rolling Huts
18381 HWY 20
Winthrop
WA 98862
United States of America
www.GoUnusual.com/rollinghuts

• Vacation rental

DOG BARK PARK INN
THE WORLDS LARGEST BEAGLE

This whimsical B&B offers two fantastic connected rooms in a one-of-a-kind giant dog, complete with his own fire hydrant

With two big dogs signaling your arrival to Dog Bark Park, visitors may walk the grounds, browse the gift shop and artists' studio featuring the chainsaw artwork of husband and wife artists Dennis and Frances. They specialize in creating folk-art style wooden canine carvings although visitors are apt to find fish, feline, bear and moose carvings as well. Over 60 different breeds and poses of dogs have been created and they can work from customer's photos to create carvings in the likeness of their canine companions.

Dennis, a self-taught chainsaw artist, has been carving for over twenty five years. Frances, who joined Dennis nearly 20 years ago, has also learned how to wield a chainsaw to carve wood into these fantastic creations. Their "big break" came in 1995 when carvings were sold on QVC television. They did nothing but carve wooden dogs for 18 months (their children barely remember seeing them during those days!). They made what seemed like a bundle of money, invested it all in developing and building Dog Bark Park, where visitors most likely will find them happily creating art.

The dog can sleep four in a combination of a queen bed in the body plus two twin foldout futon mattresses in the loft. There is a sizeable bathroom inside the dog too.

Dog Bark Park Inn offers guests an expansive continental self-serve breakfast featuring the family's secret recipe for The Prairie's Best Fruited Granola, yogurts, and their home-baked Pastries and breads.

LOCATION AND ACTIVITIES

Things to do while in Cottonwood include: Visiting the nearby Monastery of St. Gertrude. A jet-boat excursion of the Snake River and Hells Canyon, North America's deepest river canyon. Go horse-back riding or hiking in the mountains above Cottonwood. Visit the Nez Perce National Historic Park.

"Sleep in a dog"

Dog Bark Park Inn
2421 Business Loop Hwy 95
Cottonwood
Idaho
United States of America
www.GoUnusual.com/DogBarkParkInn

• Bed & Breakfast
• Recommended for children

United States of America

FEATHERBED RAILROAD
LAKESIDE RAILCARS FOR RELAXATION

Enjoy the peace and tranquility of one of nine antique railroad cabooses, each decorated with an individual theme.

You can choose from the Las Vegas bordello themed La Loose Caboose, (with it's red velvet and Mustang Ranch memorabilia) or the Art Deco styled Orient Express.

Perhaps instead you're tempted by an overnight in Easy Rider? Themed features include an "Easy Glider" chair complete with saddlebags, Harley Davidson touches, a headboard with handlebars and a quarter-scale motorcycle replica in the caboose Cupola.

Most of the cabooses feature in-room Jacuzzi tubs for two. All the cabooses are en-suite and offer individual heat and air conditioning and queen-size beds topped with a luxurious European style featherbed covers. Call with your requests for romance - or even to check on facilities for your pet. Some of the cabooses are dog friendly too!

LOCATION AND ACTIVITIES

The railcars all have an incredible view from their park-like setting under centuries-old trees, right on the shore of Lake County's Clearlake area, overlooking the private dock, boat launch and beach.

This romantic getaway is the perfect place to celebrate being in love or just enjoying the tranquility of the surroundings. You'll find a more relaxed rhythm here, whether you're on the porch of the 100-year-old Main Station or languishing in the pool.

There is a huge variety of nearby stuff to do, including almost 30 wineries, nature trails, fabulous water sports, bass fishing and great antique stores as well as peaceful, uncrowded country roads. It is the perfect place to unwind.

The Featherbed Railroad is just 120 miles north of San Francisco and about 90 minutes away from Sacramento. Also nearby are Mendocino, Healdsburg and Calistoga.

"Something for Everyone - All Aboard !"

Featherbed Railroad
2870 Lakeshore Blvd.
Nice, CA 95464
United States of America
www.GoUnusual.com/featherbedrailroad

• Bed & Breakfast

United States of America

WIGWAM MOTEL CALIFORNIA
ORIGINAL ROUTE 66 MOTEL

An update on the traditional Indian habitat of a wigwam, but in concrete, these 19 motel units near San Bernadino in California date from the early 1950's. Now recognised on the US register of historic monuments, they are part of a chain created in 1935 by Frank A. Redford. The first design in Kentucky was patented in 1936 by Frank, and the Wigwam Motel grew with one of the first franchises to include six properties across the USA following historic route 66. Only three remain in use today, San Bernardino was the last to be created - and one of the best preserved.

The wigwams were repainted and refurbished in 2003. Even though you're sleeping in a wigwam, they offer the same modern amenities - air conditioning, cable TV, private bathrooms with shower - that you'd expect of a traditional motel, just in a teepee format. All the wigwams face a central community area which provides a childrens play area and pool. Of the 19 wigwams here, the eight larger ones are set up for families, with the others available as doubles.

Breakfast isn't included although we suggest you check out one of the International House of Pancakes venues in San Bernardino or Fontana to complete your Route 66 homage.

"Eye-catching and historic!"

LOCATION AND ACTIVITIES

The postal address is in Rialto, but you're located in adjacent San Bernardino. There isn't a restaurant on site, but you're not far from options in Rialto, or San Bernardino - home to the original McDonalds hamburger - birthplace of fast food, now housing a museum of hamburger history.

Wigwam Motel California
W. Foothill Blvd.
Rialto CA
United States of America
www.GoUnusual.com/WigwamMotelCalifornia

• No Breakfast provided
• Bar / Restaurants nearby

EL COSMICO
RESTORED TRAILERS IN ICONIC SETTING

"El Cosmico is part vintage trailer, safari tent, teepee hotel and campground, part creative lab, greenhouse and amphitheatre - a community space that fosters and agitates artistic and intellectual exchange," says Liz Lambert - founder.

It is the second home to intrepid travelers and wanderers from all corners of the world. El Cosmico offers wide open spaces, a vast canopy of stars, and an inexplicable peacefulness not found in many places in the modern world.

They offer seven renovated vintage trailers each with stove, small refrigerators, fan, floor heating and hot water. You'll find they contain unique light fixtures and furnishings. If these aren't your thing (why not!), then they also offer eight safari tents and several traditional 22 ft. diameter Sioux teepees for rent. El Cosmico also offer tent camping spaces to visitors who bring a tent. Site facilities include two bathing areas, a hammock grove among the elms and a lobby store with snacks, drinks and general provisions.

If you didn't bring whatever you're looking for and can't find it here, you probably don't really need it anyways.

LOCATION AND ACTIVITIES

El Cosmico is located in Marfa (population 2121), in the high desert of West Texas. Increasingly a tourist destination in its own right, it is equally influenced by its ranching roots, proximity to Mexico and the vibrant migration of artists from big cities. Marfa sits at a unique crossroads where rural ranching culture and international art converge.

Mañana

"El Cosmico is at the center of an exodus from a world of urgency. This is not to be understood as irreverence for timeliness and progress. They believe in those things too. But life gets busy. The way you thought things would go just aren't the way they end up. Best intentions are waylaid. But it seems like sometimes the only way to make something really amazing is through a steady balance of kicking the dirt around and napping. This is what El Cosmico is about"

"El Cosmico flies its Mañana flag proudly"

El Cosmico
802 S. Highland Ave.
Marfa, TX 79843
United States of America
www.GoUnusual.com/ElCosmico

• Vacation rental

SAUGERTIES LIGHTHOUSE
LIGHTHOUSE

and associated wetland reserve for a nominal $1, in return for their agreement to restore this landmark. In 1990, the light was restored and the doors opened to the public to share this slice of history.

LOCATION AND ACTIVITIES

Saugerties Lighthouse is located 42 miles from Albany NY. As well as a bed & breakfast it contains a small museum, keeper's quarters, two bedrooms, kitchen and living room.

"Heritage property in a beautiful location"

Lying off the Hudson River, Saugerties lighthouse offers a beautiful and unusual opportunity to step back to a less rushed pace and more traditional way of life.

This 1869-built lighthouse fell into disuse in the 1950's. With the automation of the light, the original building fell into disrepair. A concerted campaign by the local villagers created a conservation trust that was able to purchase the buildings

Saugerties Lighthouse
Saugerties, NY
United States of America
www.GoUnusual.com/SaugertiesLighthouse

WINVIAN

FARMSTEAD WITH HELICOPTER IN COTTAGE

From its purchase in 1948, until its transformation into an outlet for the artistic expression of 15 professional architects, Winvian was the tranquil family farm of Winthrop and Vivian Smith. Over one weekend in 2001, the daughter-in-law and granddaughter team of Maggie and Heather Smith decided on a no-rules design competition to transform the property, engaging 15 architects to build 19 amazing cottages – each with a design history of its own.

From the "bringing the outside indoors" approach of 'Camping' to the rustic charm of 'Woodlands', each cottage on the 113 acre estate is completely unique - yet none more so than 'Helicopter'. Using a genuine, U.S. coast guard Sikorsky helicopter, rescued from Arizona, this cottage pays homage to the roots of Sikorsky in nearby Stratford. The helicopter dominates the room, with the cottage seemingly built around the outside. Even the rotor blades are embedded in the ceiling and walls. Inside the 'copter is a bar and lounge area with flat screen TV DVD and selection of movies. Never was a mission more comfortable! Clamber onto the flight deck, pull the controls and flick the switches - scramble for rescue!

The bed is to the side of the room staring straight at the Sikorsky, showing a view that was once a welcome sight for those in distress. No worry of that here. The furnishings are of a high standard and, should you require help to regain your composure, a five minute walk to the spa will sooth any frayed nerves.

Normally under 18's aren't allowed, however they are welcome on specific family friendly dates. Dogs are welcome in three of the cottages.

LOCATION AND ACTIVITIES

A couple of miles off Route 63, cottages are for couples and offer both a-la-carte pricing as well as inclusive options, with facilities, meals, soft drinks, wine and some spirits provided. The meals are plentiful. Your day, as well as your stomach, would be full if you took opportunity to try them all. Spa treatments are extra.

"A helicopter in your bedroom"

Winvian
155 Alain White Road
Morris
Connecticut 06763
United States of America
www.GoUnusual.com/Winvian

• Inclusive and a-la-carte packages available
• Bar / Restaurant on site

27

JULES' UNDERSEA LODGE
UNDERWATER HOTEL

When guests visit Jules' Undersea Lodge in Key Largo, Florida, they discover that the name is no marketing gimmick. Just to enter the Lodge, you need to scuba dive 21 feet beneath the surface of the sea. Entering through an opening in the bottom of the Lodge, the feeling is much like discovering a secret underwater clubhouse.

Starting out as the La Chalupa underwater research laboratory in the 1970's, it was one of the most advanced research habitats in the world. While special research projects are still undertaken, the site allows dive certified guests to book an overnight stay as part of a romantic celebration or proposal. Guests can explore their marine environment with scuba gear provided by the Lodge, or peer out of the large circular windows while the fish look back at you.

The cottage sized building isn't short on facilities: hot showers, a kitchen, books and music. There is even wifi!

Best creature comfort of all is that they can deliver pizza as part of your overnight programme. Extra anchovies anyone?

The interior has two living chambers, each 20 feet long and 8 feet in diameter. One chamber is divided into two 8 x 10 foot bedrooms; the other is an 8 x 20 foot common room with dining and entertainment facilities. The main feature of each room is the large round window that looks out into the lagoon. Between the two chambers is a 10 x 20 foot "wet room" entrance area with a moon pool entrance, shower and bathroom facilities.

LOCATION

Jules Undersea Lodge is located 1½ hours' drive from Miami International Airport at the bottom of the Emerald Lagoon in Key Largo Undersea Park.

"They even deliver pizza!"

Jules Undersea Lodge
Key Largo Undersea Park
51 Shoreland Dr.
Key Largo, Florida
United States of America
www.GoUnusual.com/JulesUnderseaLodge

• 24hrs on land required before flying
• Food by arrangement

United States of America

VERANA

FLOATING ABOVE THE BAY OF BANDERAS

This small hotel and spa, is as unusual as it is remote.

Open November through June, VERANA never fails to enchant guests. Luxurious yet surrounded by unadulterated nature on all sides, it is an amazing destination for weddings, honeymoons and get-away-from-it-all packages that take advantage of the fine food, setting and spa.

VERANA has just nine guesthouses dotted throughout the 5-acre property, lush with tropical plantings and fruit trees. All the guesthouses are unique in concept and feel. As Architectural Digest's Kathryn Harris said, "The bungalows are part of an ongoing play between inside and out, past and present, privacy and community, nature and manmade."

VERANA's remote and romantic setting has always drawn brides and grooms for their ceremony or just honeymoon. Special packages and a gift registry are available. The VERANA spa is fantastic for all couples and while any of the guesthouses are perfect, the most recent addition, The Tea House is the most spacious and has its own plunge pool.

The resort includes an indoor-outdoor spa designed to maximize its jungle setting. Enjoy the Watsu pool or Plain air Japanese style soaking tubs with a massage and fruit detox.

Despite the remote location, VERANA's kitchen led by Yelapan native, Chef Fabian, creates three sublime meals a day. Every other day the VERANA boat picks up supplies in Puerto Vallarta to help fashion the menu which is ingredient driven, organic where possible, and Regional Mexican in origin laced with international flavours and slickly finished with modern health consciousness.

LOCATION AND ACTIVITIES

Atop Yelapa located on Mexico's southwest coast, 30 miles south of Puerto Vallarta. Accessed by air daily via Puerto Vallarta International Airport, then taxi to Boca de Tomatlan beach where VERANA's boat transports guests to Yelapa.

"Designer retreat and spa resort"

VERANA
Calle Zaragoza No 404
Puerto Vallarta
Jalisco
Mexico
www.GoUnusual.com/VERANA

- Group & Packaged trips only
- 2 night min stay
- Full board dining

MAJAHUITAS RESORT
BEACH VILLAS IN AN UNSPOILT AREA OF COASTLINE

LOCATION AND ACTIVITIES

Breakfast, Lunch and Dinner are included in the price. Guests can also enjoy free of charge: beach volleyball, table tennis, snorkeling, kayaking, and a guided hike to the Quimixto waterfall.

"Seclusion and tranquility in get-away location"

Majahuitas Resort is an eco-friendly boutique hotel located on one of the most secluded beaches in the Bay of Bandera's, half an hour south of Puerto Vallarta. There are no roads or electricity at Majahuitas and it is open between October and June. It is only accessible by boat and they rely on solar power for energy.

The eight casitas face the ocean so that you may enjoy the fabulous views, the gentle breeze and sounds of the sea. The first thing you'll see as you wake up is the white sand beach and crystal waters. Each room is decorated with handmade wood furniture, tile floors and Mexican pottery.

Majahuitas Resort
Conocido Playa Majahuitas S/N
Puerto Vallarta
Jalisco 48310
Mexico
www.GoUnusual.com/MajahuitasResort

- Packaged trips only
- Full board dining

XINALANI RETREAT

WELLNESS, YOGA AND SELF DISCOVERY IN ECO SETTING

Xinalani was conceived as a tropical haven to host mind-body-soul retreats for individuals, couples and groups in search of a one-of-a-kind experience made of adventure, exclusive contact with nature and inner-discovery. Featuring a state-of-the-art Studio, specially designed for the practice of Yoga and other physical and spiritual disciplines. Immersed in a natural environment of spectacular views, the resort is filled with a serenity that allows guests to discover - and reawaken a more balanced lifestyle.

Born out of the vision of a Mexican-French family with a strong anchor in Architecture, Interior Design, Yoga, Surf and Adventure, Xinalani opened in October 2010 and has offered guests a relaxing WOW ever since.

Offering sea views, spacious palm thatched villas float on stilts. These luxurious handmade eco-chic suites are surrounded by lush jungle, edging a pristine beach, with the only access by boat (a shuttle service is available). The resorts is open October to June.

LOCATION AND ACTIVITIES

Xinalani is a private all-suites resort hidden on a pristine beach, surrounded by a luxuriant jungle on the south shore of Banderas Bay, in Puerto Vallarta, Mexico. Each guest can feel the intimate closeness to the natural elements and receive well-deserved personal attention.

The Retreat is about discovery, admiration, love for yoga, nature, conscious travel, wellness, and mindful living. Xinalani aims to reveal the beauty of an unknown Mexico and create eye-opening vacations.

All the accommodation are beachfront, spacious, palm-thatched cabins floating on stilts. Suites were designed with refined elegance and built and furnished by local artisans. Their cozy interiors inspire feelings of calm and serenity. You will enjoy the closeness of the natural elements, the stimulation of the open-air private showers and the stunning views of Puerto Vallarta and the Pacific Ocean from your terrace.

Suites are designed for double occupancy, however, people are allowed to share double beds to make triple or quadruple occupancy.

"Unplug while you enjoy the sensation of the sea breeze from your hammock at this yoga retreat"

Xinalani Retreat
Playa el Volador
Quimixto,Near Puerta Vallarta
Jalisco 48399
Mexico
www.GoUnusual.com/XinalaniRetreat

- Packaged trips only
- 2 night min stay
- Full board dining

ADDITIONAL PROPERTIES
NORTH AMERICA

CANADA
Algonquin Eco-Lodge
Algonquin Provincial Park, Ontario
Canada
Wilderness & Eco enthusiast dream lodge, surrounded by forests and trails
www.GoUnusual/AlgonquinEco-Lodge

Fantasyland Hotel
Edmonton
Canada
Several themed rooms available in this hotel, mall and amusement park
www.GoUnusual/FantasylandHotel

Hôtel de Glace - Canada
Sainte-Catherine-De-La-Jacques-Cartier, Quebec
Canada
The Ice Hotel: an exceptional winter event that is unique in America
www.GoUnusual/HoteldeGlace-Canada

King Pacific Lodge
Princess Royal Island, Vancouver
Canada
Floating hotel luxury in the heart of the Canadian wilderness
www.GoUnusual/KingPacificLodge

UNITED STATES OF AMERICA
Alaska's Tree House
Seward, Alaska
United States of America
Treehouse property, with outdoor views of towering spruce
www.GoUnusual/AlaskasTreeHouse

Beckham Creek Cave Haven
Arkansas
United States of America
Totally secluded cave dwelling, with underground Jaccuzzi's for relaxation
www.GoUnusual/BeckhamCreekCaveHaven

Cedar Creek Treehouse
Ashford, Washington
United States of America
Eco friendly mountain retreat with tree house accommodation
www.GoUnusual/CedarCreekTreehouse

Costanoa Coastal Lodge & Camp
Pescadero, California
United States of America
Tented cabins overlooking rolling coastal hills in Southern California
www.GoUnusual/CostanoaCoastalLodgeandCamp

Cove Haven Entertainment resorts
Lakeville, Pennsylvania
United States of America
All-Inclusive resorts offering romance and luxury with heart-shaped beds, pools and famous champagne glass Jacuzzi's
www.GoUnusual/CoveHavenEntertainmentresorts

Dunton Hot Springs
Dolores, CO
United States of America
Restored ghost town spa resort, offering outdoor living and away-from-it-all surroundings in this old gold rush town
www.GoUnusual/DuntonHotSprings

East Brother Light Station
East Brother Island, California
United States of America
Victorian style lighthouse, restored and converted to hotel
www.GoUnusual/EastBrotherLightStation

Hana Lani
Hana, Maui, Hawaii
United States of America
Treehouses in an ocean view setting
www.GoUnusual/HanaLani

ADDITIONAL PROPERTIES
NORTH AMERICA

UNITED STATES OF AMERICA continued
Heceta Head Lighthouse
92072 Hwy. 101 South
Yachats
Oregon
United States of America
Considered by many as one of the most beautiful lighthouses in the world, the adjoining cottage is your luxury B+B
www.GoUnusual/HecetaHeadLighthouse

Historic Union Station
Indianapolis, Indiana
United States of America
Renovated railroad station, listed in National Register of Historic Places
www.GoUnusual/HistoricUnionStation-Indianapolis

Karrels Double K Ranch
Tucson, Arizona
United States of America
Restored cabooses in the garden, with outdoor miniature garden railway for enthusiasts to enjoy
www.GoUnusual/KarrelsDoubleKRanch

Kokopelli's Cave
Farmington
New Mexico
United States of America
Wilderness cave dwelling, blasted out of mountain for spectacular views
www.GoUnusual/KokopellisCave

Library Hotel
New York
United States of America
Each floor dedicated to a category of reading, and bedrooms to a theme
www.GoUnusual/LibraryHotel

Madonna Inn
San Luis Obispo, California
United States of America
Amazing designer property with every room tastefully different, from caveman rooms with waterfall showers to daisy themed rooms
www.GoUnusual/MadonnaInn

Nickelodeon Family Suites
Orlando, Florida
United States of America
Nickelodeon themed hotel with integral water park for children
www.GoUnusual/NickelodeonFamilySuites

Northern Rail Train Car Hotel
Two Harbors, Minnesota
United States of America
Sleep in converted railway goods wagons
www.GoUnusual/NorthernRailTrainCarHotel

Out'n'About Treesort and Treehouse Institute
Cave Junction, OR
United States of America
Treehouse facilities and fun with this advocate of outdoor living
www.GoUnusual/OutnAboutTreesortandTreehouseInstitute

Post Ranch Inn
Big Sur, California
United States of America
Ocean view escape with tree house and cabin accommodation
www.GoUnusual/PostRanchInn

Vista Caballo
Dove Creek, Colorado
United States of America
Where horses and the great outdoors energise your soul
www.GoUnusual/VistaCaballo

ADDITIONAL PROPERTIES
NORTH AMERICA

UNITED STATES OF AMERICA continued
Wickwood Country Inn
Saugatuck, Michigan
United States of America
Best selling cookbook author hideaway with fantastic food
www.GoUnusual/WickwoodCountryInn

Wigwam Motel Arizona
Holbrook, AZ
United States of America
Historic Wigwam motel, still run by the founders family
www.GoUnusual/WigwamMotelArizona

MEXICO
Quinta Real Zacatecas
Zacatecas
Mexico
Converted bullring, now luxury hotel combining history with service
www.GoUnusual/QuintaRealZacatecas

"Twenty years from now you will be more disappointed by the things you didn't do than by the ones you did do. So throw off the bowlines, sail away from the safe harbor. Catch the trade winds in your sails. Explore. Dream. Discover."

Mark Twain

South America

Belize, Costa Rica, Panama, Brazil, Argentina

Key

Entries in **Bold** typeface indicate full page entries with a photo.
Others are additional indexed entries.

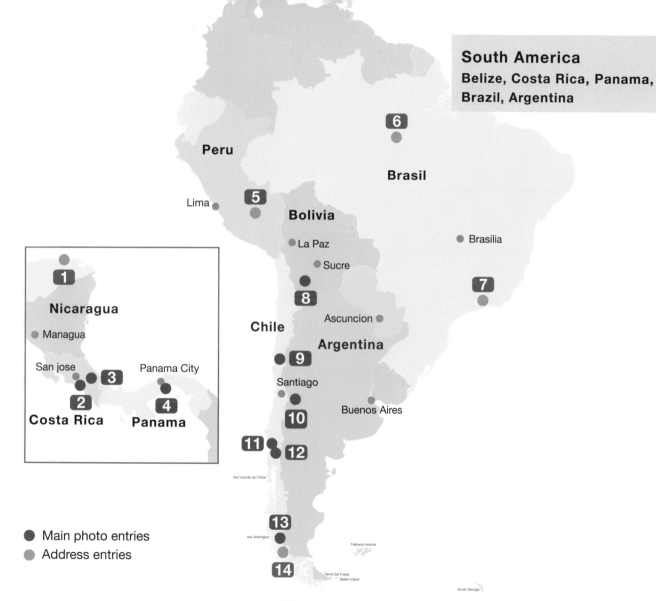

South America
Belize, Costa Rica, Panama, Brazil, Argentina

Peru

6

Brasil

Lima

5

Bolivia

La Paz

Brasilia

Sucre

8

7

Ascuncion

Chile

Argentina

9

Santiago

Buenos Aires

10

11

12

Isla Grande de Chiloe

13

Isla Wellington

Falkland Islands

Tierra Del Fuego
Staton Island

South Georgia

Nicaragua

Managua

San jose

3

Panama City

2

4

Costa Rica

Panama

● Main photo entries
● Address entries

COSTA VERDE
727 JET CONVERTED INTO LUXURY ACCOMMODATION

LOCATION AND ACTIVITIES

Four totally unique bars & restaurants will satisfy your every taste and need. From the social scene at El Avión - a Fairchild C-123 transporter converted to a bar, to peaceful, breathtaking views of Anaconda, to the music & barbecue at La Cantina to the casual dining & wood-fired pizza at El Wagon – Costa Verde has something special for all tastes!

Costa Rica's Pacific coast enjoys a classic, predictable monsoon climate. There are only two distinct seasons: rainy and dry. Normally the rainy season runs from mid-April to mid-November. During this time, mornings are usually clear and it often rains in the early evenings.

"First Class comfort, now retired from flying duties"

The Costa Verde team have transported and refurbished a 1965 vintage Being 727 airframe to create a fantastic, two bedroom suite in this resort - a favourite for weddings, honeymoons and romance. Set out on a concrete plinth that juts up 50 feet into the jungle canopy, you'll feel like you're flying when you look out of the windows. Furnishings are hand carved teak, and the rear bedroom has a handcrafted deck atop the wing.

In it's former life under the colours of South Africa Air and latterly Avianca Airlines (Colombia), it shuttled the well heeled to exotic destinations. Now refitted with custom built luxuries and en suite facilities it once again caters to the needs of pampered travellers.

Costa Verde Resort
Puerto Quepos
Quepos
Costa Rica
www.GoUnusual.com/CostaVerde

NATURE OBSERVATORIO
TROPICAL FOREST TREEHOUSE OVERLOOKING CARIBBEAN

A two storey treehouse, with modern conveniences and comforts, powered by solar energy and using collected rainwater, suspended 25 metres in the rainforest canopy.

The first level has a 360° view to the jungle and the Caribbean sea with hammocks and sofas. Not a single nail or screw was used to secure the structure, which is held in place by strong nylon webbing. Built from the top down, it has two double bedrooms while a hatch in the top room provides access to the very top of the tree Observatorio, a further 30m above you.

Upstairs the two comfortable bedrooms have queen size beds, and downstairs is your viewing platform, where binoculars and a telescope are provided, let you watch the nature around. The 360° panoramic vista encompasses the surrounding greenery, as well as the Caribbean Ocean stretching out to the Eastern horizon, and the blue tropical sky.

Rainwater supplies the Observatorio's modern bathroom which has a dry flush eco-toilet. Solar energy provides electricity for the usual home conveniences.

LOCATION AND ACTIVITIES

Located in the jungle of the Manzanillo – Gandoca wildlife refuge of Costa Rica, on the top of a small hill. From Manzanillo, it is around a 5 minute drive and then 30 minute walk through the jungle to where you'll see incredible wildlife including; poison dart-frogs, sloths, monkeys, toucans, and lot more!

The Observatorio provides an electric car for guests to go to the village of Manzanillo for beaches, shops and restaurants.

"Don't worry about having to climb yourself. The solar collectors also power an electric winch"

Nature Observatorio
Puerto Viejo
Limon 7304
Costa Rica
www.GoUnusual.com/NatureObservatorio

• Resort Property
• Packaged tours available

CANOPY TOWER
DISUSED RADAR TOWER IN RAINFOREST

Built in 1965 by the United States Air Force to house radar used in the defence of the Panama Canal, the tower was demilitarized and transferred to Panamá in 1996. Located on top of Semaphore Hill, in the heart of the semi-deciduous Soberanía National Park, it rises above the tree canopy. Dominating the roof is the 30 foot (10m) high geodesic dome with an observation deck surrounding it from which you can see the Pacific entrance to the Panama Canal and the skyline of Panama City. The top floor is used as the main dining area, and is completely surrounded by panoramic windows. The second and first floors provide the living space with en-suite bathrooms and large windows to observe lower levels of the forest canopy.

You are never more than 40 feet from the birds and should pack earplugs if you are a light sleeper and don't wish to be woken at first light. Dawn awakens the birds on this migratory route and you'll have ample opportunity to see birds normally glimpsed high in the tops of trees, right outside your room.

Your host is the friendly Raúl Arias de Para, who not only is knowledgeable about the birds and wildlife, he is a teller of some great lighthearted stories over evening drinks.

LOCATION AND ACTIVITIES

If you're not a bird watching fan yourself, then the activities of the Panama canal are likely to be the main attraction. There are two sets of locks on the Pacific side of the Canal, Miraflores and Pedro Miguel a short drive from the Tower, as well as the Panama Canal Visitor Centre.

There are 12 rooms in the tower and the 2-3 person suites on the 2nd floor have best views. Canopy Tower does not accommodate children younger than 13 years of age.

It takes only about 30-45 minutes to drive to the Canopy Tower from Panama City and one hour from Tucumen International Airport. You can get within a mile (2km) of the tower by public transport, although should ask for exact directions so that the bus driver can drop you off nearby.

"…provides view of rainforest birds in tree canopy"

Canopy Tower Ecolodge and Nature Observatory
Semaphore Hill
Semaphore Hill Road
Soberanía National Park
Panama
www.GoUnusual.com/CanopyTowerEcolodgeandNatureObservatory

• Packaged trips only
• 2 night min stay
• Full board dining

PALACIO DE SAL
HOTEL MADE OF SALT

Palacio de Sal Hotel, newly remodeled and unique in the world, is completely built in salt. Walls, floors, ceilings, and most of the furniture too, are all made of salt.

The property offers 16 rooms (8 double rooms and 8 twin bedded) with private bath, solarium, central heating and electricity in every room. Facilities include a Games Room with Billiards.

Pensu, the fairway and playing area are salt crust and the green is granular salt. If you enjoy playing different courses, this must rate as one of the more extreme!

LOCATION AND ACTIVITIES

Located at the port of Colchani, on the east coast of the salt flats, only 25 kms from Uyuni town. Covering 12.000km² the Uyuni salt flats are the biggest salt desert on earth, at an altitude of 3650 meters above sea level.

Seasonally, there is a unique 9-hole Par 36 golf course here, open from May to November. Designed by Christian

"A completely different way to view the amazing landscape and stunning sunsets of the Salar de Uyuni"

Palacio de Sal
Salar de Uyuni
Uyuni, Potosi
Bolivia
www.GoUnusual.com/PalaciodeSal

• Breakfast provided
• Bar / Restaurant on site

ELQUI DOMOS

ASTRONOMY RESORT OFFERING HORSEBACK STARGAZING TOURS

Born as a dream between the owner Esteban Zárate and his wife, and located in the famous Elqui Valley which is well known for it's clear sky, this Astronomy themed hotel offers night sky horseriding tours and your own telescope.

Built around the dream of watching the stars from your bed, Esteban discovered geodesic domes on holiday, and said: "that's it!". Leaving his job as a Regional Director of the National Tourism Board the journey to Elqui Domos began.

Wanting guests to enjoy their dream and learn from the sky at the same time, they've included telescopes in each room and can share their passion and knowledge of the heavens.

The dome tents have everything inside: a full bathroom, comfortable beds, heating, snack bar etc. but you should still dress warmly. Night temperatures can drop to below freezing during winter nights (down to -10° C). However, cold air makes for clear skies, and the absence of light pollution in the remote location makes viewing conditions close to ideal.

The two storey domes have a living room and bathroom on the ground floor. Upstairs is the main bed with detachable roof. Each dome also has a large terrace and you are provided with a quality telescope to use. You'll also find a stocked fridge, tea and coffee facilities as well as maps and magazines about astronomy.

Their on-site restaurant, Carinae (named after the most beautiful star you can see from the Southern Hemisphere) serves fusion food using local produce. Daylight provides an opportunity for picnics and barbecues by the river.

For those unfamiliar with night skies, Esteban and his team provide a stargazing tour and telescope-operating session to help you get the best from your evening viewings. They can also arrange a horseback stargazing tour, which should not be missed.

LOCATION AND ACTIVITIES

Elqui Domos is about 1 ½ hours drive (96 km/60 miles) from the nearest large town of La Serena, on a road that is paved for all but the last 3 km (2 miles).

"Telescope provided for best starry night views"

Elqui Domos
Camino Público Pisco Elqui KM 3.5
Pisco Elqui
Chile
www.GoUnusual.com/ElquiDomos

- Breakfast provided
- Bar / Restaurant on site

CASA MARGOT HOTEL CHAMPAGNERIE
CHAMPAGNE THEMED HOTEL IN AWARD WINNING WINERY

Created when the founders of Casa Margot understood it wasn't enough to simply show and talk about the process for the production of their Champagne process sparkling wines. True appreciation required visitors to take the time to "feel" the process with the intangible values of good Champagne: glamour, luxury, patience, history, art - so they opened Hotel Champagnerie.

The concept "champagnerie" emerged as the appropriate one for such an aim: a placid place, secluded, with wide gardens, old groves and artistic influence, that will accompany you while you taste the exquisite beverage of kings, and be better able to understand and appreciate Champagne. Margot Winery has specialized in the production of high-quality sparkling wines since 2003, using time honoured French techniques. Estate production has introduced the culture of Champagne to a palate conscious Argentinean audience, winning awards and friends.

Casa Margot offers luxury accommodation, with personalized attention, professional and bilingual, offered by the family that owns the Hotel. Guided tastings by a professional oenologist can be arranged, as well as wine matching with delicious dishes. A French-Argentine breakfast with croissant and home-made bread is served in the Atelier – a room influenced by tango and Buenos Aires. A welcome glass of champagne is served in the evening, along with a brief theatrical piece that expresses the secrets of this luxurious beverage.

From a romantic dinner of Argentine gourmet cuisine, matched with the most delicious wines in the candlelit Margot Deli Bistro to a soirée of Sushi & Jazz with champagne lying in the comfortable cushions of Marlen loft, everything in Casa Margot achieves a once-in-a-lifetime experience that fills the spirit, satisfying even the greatest expectations.

Location & Activities

The house is influenced by the famous and beloved Mendocinean sculptor Eliana Molinelli, whose works are recognized worldwide.

Casa Margot Hotel Champagnerie
Italia 6016, Chacras de Coria
Lujan de Cuyo
MENDOZA
Argentina
www.GoUnusual.com/CasaMargotHotelChampagnerie

• Breakfast provided
• Bar / Restaurant on site

HOTEL ANTUMALAL

BAUHAUS STYLE LUXURY PROPERTY WITH SPA AND STUNNING VIEWS

LOCATION AND ACTIVITIES

The hotel was built on a rough and challenging rocky hillside, only 2 km from Pucón. The construction of Antumalal began in 1945 and the hotel was a pioneer in the development of Pucón as an important tourist center.

Chilean airlines fly in only one hour from Santiago daily to Temuco. From Temuco you can rent a car or request a transfer to the hotel, which is about an hour and a half away.

"The landscape is framed in each room"

On a wooded point overlooking the lake, between gardens, terraces, and waterfalls sits Hotel Antumalal. In the style of the 1950's, the furniture blends native wood, iron, and rope, creating a unique style. Meaning "corral of the sun" in the ancient mapuche language, Antumalal's vibrant and modern architecture fits harmoniously with its setting. The main sitting room extends above a cliff with an entire wall of glass overlooking the lake. Wood-paneled walls, soft white carpets and an immense fireplace create an elegant yet simple ambiance. This property is so elegant that it has hosted visits from a star studded guest list, including Queen Elizabeth II.

Each of the 22 rooms has a wall-sized window and is paneled with native wood. Each warmed by a fireplace, they offer a cozy environment from where you can enjoy spectacular views of Lake Villarrica.

Hotel Antumalal
Km 2 Camino Pucón-Villarrica
Pucon, IX Region
Chile
www.GoUnusual.com/HotelAntumalal

• Breakfast provided
• Bar / Excellent restaurant on site

MAGIC MOUNTAIN HOTEL
FOREST ACCOMMODATION IN A MANMADE, FAIRYTALE MOUNTAIN

Originally a place for friends to stay while they enjoyed the hunting and fishing resources of the Hulio Hulio reserve, the name is from a favourite book of the owners. The story describes a mountain that has magical powers and grants wishes – The Magic Mountain. With a waterfall cascading from the pinnacle of the roof, the lodge is indeed a special place.

While you're some way from civilization, the lodge is self-sufficient and has a restaurant "Meson del Bosque" - The Forest Table. All meals are taken here and you'll get the opportunity to sample some really good Chilean cooking.

A recommendation for those with a sweet tooth is to try it with sugar but beware! Too large a portion will leave you unable to do anything except snooze. During the evening the restaurant provides a bar where you can enjoy the traditional Chilean Pisco Sour. Made of grape liqueur, mixed with lemon juice and sugar it is particularly refreshing. Take care however, Pisco Sour is easy to drink and a hangover this far from a pharmacy is particularly painful if you've forgotten to pack aspirin.

Rooms: Each of the 13 rooms has a private bathroom. There are also 11 cabins, accommodating between 4 and 6 people. Rooms are named with plants and animals found in the park, although a little detective work with a good dictionary is required to try and translate some of the more obscure. "Lahuen" is a medical plant used by the local Mapuches Indians and "Ranita de Darwin", a tiny frog close to extinction.

LOCATION AND ACTIVITIES

The Lodge is 35 miles (60km) from Panguipulli, the nearest town. The largest major city is Valdivia, around 80 miles (165km) from the resort. "Pichol" airport is there and you should plan for a transfer of about 2½ hours by car. The other airport is in Temuco, 85 miles (180km) away – around 3 hours from Huilo Huilo.

The Lodge is located between two small villages, Puerto Fuy and Neltume. You can find small restaurants, plus craft shops selling furniture and animal sculpture here. The area is famous for fishing and hunting in summer and ski randonée on the volcano in winter. They have also constructed a 500m aerial ropeway up to 90m high in the forest canopy, allowing you to travel from tree to tree, over cliffs with traverses.

"Designed around a Chilean fairytale story"

Magic Mountain Hotel
Huilo-Huilo
Panguipulli
Chile
www.GoUnusual.com/MagicMountainHotel

• Breakfast provided
• Bar / Restaurant on site

ECOCAMP PATAGONIA
GEODESIC DOMES IN TORRES DEL PAINE

Patagonia´s first fully sustainable accommodation and the world's first Geodesic hotel, EcoCamp opened its eco-friendly doors in 2001 and has been welcoming trekkers and nature lovers ever since. EcoCamp offers upscale camping in domes inspired by the region's ancient nomadic inhabitants, resistant to the wild Patagonian outdoors and utilizing sophisticated green technology. Guests trek through scenic landscapes by day past rivers, glaciers, mountains and wildlife, and relax in EcoCamp's domes at night with delicious food and wine.

EcoCamp has 25 bedroom domes in total and 3 large community domes where guests eat breakfast and dinner overlooking the towers and unwind in the bar in the evening or plan excursions in the library.

The 13 standard domes have a cosy 10m² interior and come equipped with fleece sheets, blankets and feather quilts. Guests can upgrade to a 23m² superior dome with a private bathroom and gas heater, or choose one of the 10 Suite domes which are 28m² with an en-suite bathroom, low-emission wood stove, bathroom heater and outdoor terrace..

LOCATION AND ACTIVITIES

Patagonia is a vast and diverse region, with scenery ranging from dramatic mountain formations and smoky volcanoes to flat barren pampa and expansive ice fields. These lands are crowded with glaciers, lakes, fjords, ancient forests and wildlife such as guanacos, flamingos, condors, ñandus and huemules and also offer some of the most magnificent trekking and nature in the world.

The Torres del Paine National Park in Chile is home to an incredible array of wildlife and exciting Patagonian tours including the W Trek and the Paine Circuit.

EcoCamp runs specialist trekking tours and wildlife trips with nights spent at EcoCamp Patagonia.

"Sleep in harmony with nature"

Eco Camp Patagonia
Torres Del Paine National Park
Patagonia
Chile
www.GoUnusual.com/EcoCampPatagonia

• Resort Property
• Packaged tours available

ADDITIONAL PROPERTIES
BELIZE, BRAZIL, CHILE, PERU

BELIZE
Parrot Nest Lodge
San Ignacio, Cayo
Belize
Thatched tree houses in Belize for starlight views in a woodland location
www.GoUnusual/ParrotNestLodge

BRAZIL
Ariau Amazon Towers Hotel
Manaus
Brazil
Worlds largest treehouse complex in Amazon Rainforest
www.GoUnusual/AriauAmazonTowersHotel

Exploranter – Overland Hotel
Sao Paulo
Brazil
A hotel on wheels that tours the South America
www.GoUnusual/ExploranterOverlandHotel

CHILE
Indigo Patagonia Hotel and Spa
Puerto Natales
Chile
Stylish destination where travellers mix with intrepid mountaineers and climbers
www.GoUnusual/IndigoPatagoniaHotelAndSpa

PERU
Machu Pichu Sanctuary
Cusco
Peru
Some of the best views in the world of this ancient Inca settlement
www.GoUnusual/MachuPichuSanctuary

"Take only memories,

leave only footprints."

POLICIA FEDERAL - BRASIL

0 2 11 11   283 2

CLAS.   DOC   PRAZO

Chief Seattle

Scandinavia

Iceland, Finland, Norway, Sweden, Denmark

Key

Entries in **Bold** typeface indicate full page entries with a photo.
Others are additional indexed entries.

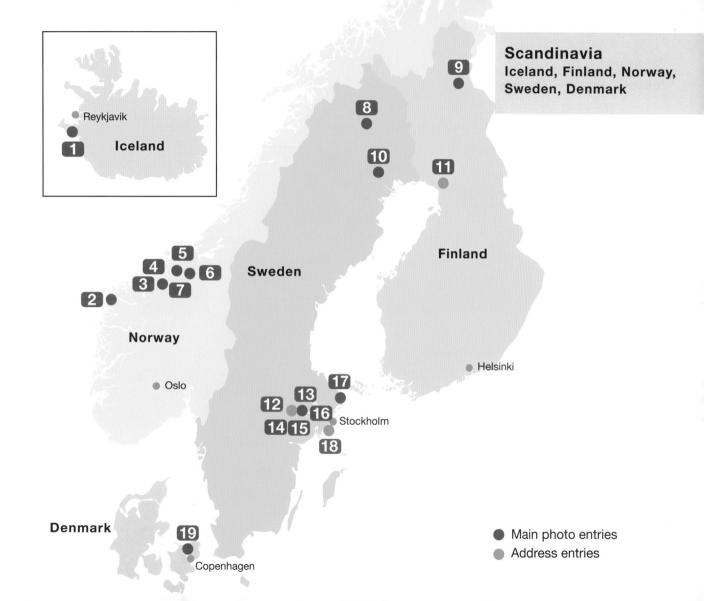

Reykjavik

Iceland

1

Scandinavia
Iceland, Finland, Norway,
Sweden, Denmark

9

8

10

11

5

4

6

Sweden

3

7

Finland

2

Norway

Oslo

Helsinki

17

12

13

16

14

15

Stockholm

18

Denmark

19

Copenhagen

● Main photo entries
● Address entries

HOTEL VIKING
VIKING AND FAROE ISLAND THEMED HOTEL

LOCATION AND ACTIVITIES

Only 10 minutes by car from the center of Reykjavik, groups activities include the Viking Kidnap managed by artists dressed as Viking warriors, taking place in a traditional setting fit for Vikings and guests. Set up for coach parties, they provide an adventure and welcome drink the Viking way! There will be singing and the opportunity to quench your thirst with Viking warriors offering "Mead" to drink - Viking Beer.

"Discover Viking heritage"

Traditionally furnished Hotel Viking has rooms with a Viking theme, as well rooms featuring art and local crafts of West Nordic countries including Greenland and the Faroe Islands.

Recently added are 14 family friendly Viking cabins decorated with traditional crafts, but featuring modern bathroom facilities. The hotel has a rock walled sauna and spa pool as well as a cave room used for Viking events, popular with coach tours and groups.

Hotel Viking
Strandgata 55
Hafnarfjordur, Reykjavik 200
Iceland
www.GoUnusual.com/HotelViking

SVINOEY LIGHTHOUSE
RUGGED ISLAND WITH HELICOPTER ACCESS

Svinoey is a unique environment in of the most distinctive and unusual locations in the world. With rugged beauty and solitude, it is for those who want to experience something really exclusive. Ideal for that special conference, meeting or a gathering of a group of friends.

Svinoey does not feature "normal" hotel facilities. It is a "house/home" environment, with a full-time person providing for your needs.

The location makes Svinoy lighthouse one of the most extreme experiences that you can find. The (now automated) lighthouse was manned for 100 years, from 1905 to 2005, and has been a meteorological observation station since 1955. Weather data from Svinoy lighthouse is still used to ensure meteorologic accuracy. The raw power and beauty of nature is seldom closer at hand. Svinoey lighthouse is one of the few places in the world where sunsets and hurricanes are equally fascinating.

Svinoey can accommodate up to 11 people (4 double rooms plus 3 single rooms). You have the entire 900 metre long island to yourself, staying in the house which once was utilised by the lighthouse keepers.

Pricing is entirely based upon your requirements, and includes helicopter transport and a permanent staff member/cook who will accompany you and ensure your safety.

LOCATION AND ACTIVITIES

Svinoey is located in open water 12 nautical miles off the Norwegian coast, in an area known locally for some of the wildest weather that Norway can offer.

The island can be reached by boat from the sea, but due to the power and volatility of the waves in this region, for safety reasons, access is by helicopter only for pre-arranged groups.

"Wild and beautiful get-away-from-it-all retreat! "

Svinoey Lighthouse
Svinøy Fyr
Herøy
Norway
www.GoUnusual.com/SvinoeyLighthouse

• Packaged trips only
• Full board catering

MOLJA LIGHTHOUSE
150 YEAR-OLD LIGHTHOUSE AT HARBOUR ENTRANCE

Molja lighthouse is positioned at the end of a 100 metre sea wall, creating an experience that is entirely unique. You are able to experience the seclusion of a tiny building facing the power of nature, while at the same time remaining close to the center of town. Some say that it is even better to stay during a winter storm, than on a beautiful summer's day. Whatever the weather, it is a memorable and romantic place to stay.

The interior of the lighthouse is completely round, only 3 meters in diameter, but through effective use of the available spaces, Molja now boasts a bedroom upstairs and a bathroom downstairs. The design was carried out by Snohetta, Norway's most well known architects - (designers of Oslo Opera House and Ground Zero museum in the New York City among many other landmark projects). They have carefully achieved a wonderful blend of modern and spacious bathroom facilities with a cosy bedroom and rustic interior.

Molja Fyr is run and administered by the nearby Hotel Brosundet, an easy 10 minutes walk away. With 46 rooms in the 100 year old protected building of Hotel Brosundet (see separate entry), Molja Fyr has become known locally as "Room 47". Full hotel facilities are available from the main hotel , including the Maki Restaurant, which has established a superb reputation for its fresh seafood.

Breakfast for Molja Fyr guests is either the buffet provided at Hotel Brosundet, or best of all, one delivered by bike to your door at a time of your choice.

"A romantic lighthouse of your own"

LOCATION AND ACTIVITIES

Ålesund is a charming town comprising many protected Art Nouveau style buildings, built after a catastrophic town fire in 1904. It was recently voted the most picturesque town in Norway and is a favourite in the summer months of cruise lines, receiving some 70,000 passengers annually.

Situated on islands, the town is surrounded by contrasting scenery. To the west, a chain of islands creates a rocky shelter and gives Ålesund a remote haven from the rough North Sea. To the east the sun rises from behind the snow-capped Sunnmøre Alps.

Molja Lighthouse
Brunholmgata 1
Ålesund
Norway
www.GoUnusual.com/MoljaLighthouse

• Breakfast provided
• Restaurants nearby

HOTEL BROSUNDET
DOCKSIDE WAREHOUSE CONVERTED TO BOUTIQUE HOTEL

FOOD! The old warehouse, used for the storage and treatment of salted fish right up to the 1980's is, yet again, receiving seafood from the North Sea. The seafood restaurant, Maki, recognised as one of Norway's best restaurants, completes your stay at Hotel Brosundet. This time the seafood is not just passing through the warehouse, but enhanced to ambrosial dishes by Maki chefs. Maki's ideology prides itself on creative and innovative use of the region's fish and seafood.

The menu changes every 14 days. A challenge for creative chefs, and an exploration for the guest.

LOCATION AND ACTIVITIES

Hotel Brosundet is nestled amidst residential homes, distinguished shops, seabirds, and boats. It is in the heart of Ålesund, yet at a comforting distance from busy streets. Everything is within walking distance. Five minutes on your feet can take you to a glassblower workshop, concert venue, bank, café, church, art and Art Nouveau museum, or shopping centre.

Sense history when you gaze out the windows of Hotel Brosundet as 100 years ago you would have been waiting for a fishing-boat to deliver its catch.

Each room is unique, designed by the world-famous architects "Snøhetta", who designed the Opera House in Oslo and the library in Alexandria. The result is a truly special experience.

Rooms are tastefully decorated to retain the character of the property, with clean Nordic style and modern facilities.

The hotel is in the old seafront building on Brosundet, built in Art Nouveau style following the catastrophic town fire of 1904. It is one of only ten buildings in Ålesund that are protected by a conservation order to preserve this unique architecture.

"Peaceful, restrained, full of character"

Hotel Brosundet
Skansekaia
Ålesund
Norway
www.GoUnusual.com/HotelBrosundet

- Breakfast provided
- Bar / Excellent Restaurant on site

STORFJORD HOTEL
A PEARL HIDDEN IN THE FJORDS

Storfjord Hotel's atmosphere and warmth is unique, offering traditional and luxurious accommodation. Overlooking the breathtaking Storfjord and Sunnmøre Alps, the hotel was hand built by skilled craftsmen using traditional Lafta (cross logging with whole timbers). This method of building has been part of Norway's culture for hundreds of years and houses still stand today after many generations. Modern technology lends a helping hand and provides hi-tech amenities but trusted techniques give the building it's soul. The hotel has twenty two spacious rooms all individual in design, each with luxury bathroom suite and some with classical four poster beds. Every room has a balcony with magnificent views.

Dinner is served in the timbered hall and drinks can be enjoyed in a relaxed atmosphere on the gallery landing overlooking Glomset Bay, Storfjord and the Alps.

LOCATION AND ACTIVITIES

Set in six acres of private grounds, Storfjord Hotel overlooks the dramatic and stunning Sunnmøre Alps, amidst thousands of acres of protected forest that lie between three mountains and a lake. From the hotel front door there are beautiful walks in every direction and within a short driving distance the choice is vast.

With a location at the gateway to the famous 'Golden Route' driving circuit, Storfjord Hotel provides access to some of the worlds most breathtaking scenery including UNESCO World Heritage site Geirangerfjord - "The World's most beautiful fjord".

A circular drive takes you through villages nestling in the valleys, high mountains and deep fjords.

The local mountain walks are suitable for everyone, but the more adventurous can take a ferry crossing to the rugged mountains of the Sunnmøre Alps where you can walk to a much higher altitude. Here, there is an abundance or world class hiking trails that have some of the best fjord views in all of Norway.

"Peaceful enjoyment of fantastic scenery"

Storfjord Hotel
Øvre Glomset
Skodje
Norway
www.GoUnusual.com/Storfjordhotel

• Breakfast provided
• Dinner available on request

JUVET
LANDSCAPE HOTEL

Turning design hotel convention on it's head, Juvet offers guests an understated, dark and bare room interior – to enhance the natural landscape views from the panoramic windows. Head Architect of Oslo based designers Jensen & Skodvin explains, "We wanted to give the feeling that you're outside even though you're protected inside."

At first perhaps, these minimalist pine and glass-clad buildings seem haphazardly erected, yet the views from their panoramic windows demonstrate that their locations have been expertly and specifically orientated to a particular vista. Some overlook the surrounding forest, others focus on nature-sculpted bounders, providing serenity as in a traditional Zen garden. You can almost feel the trees brushing against you, the snow-white drops of spray from the river Valldøla on your face.

LOCATION AND ACTIVITIES

Inside each of the seven cabins, the timber walls are bare of any decoration with minimal furniture – a bed, lamp and couple of designer chairs. The interior is dark to avoid taking attention away from the scenery, with only the bathroom a shocking canary yellow theme.

Treading lightly on the landscape, the rooms are anchored with removable steel rod foundations. "We are guests in nature, so it's a good idea that hotels can be taken away without leaving scars behind," Architect Jensen explains.

The spa has impressive views from the sauna and the hot tub embedded in the wooden decking alongside the river.

"Bringing the outside into your room"

Juvet
landskapshotell
Alstad,
Norway
www.GoUnusual.com/Juvet

HOTEL UNION ØYE

ARISTOCRATIC LUXURY OF A BYGONE AGE

The year is 1891. The aristocracy and upper classes of Europe are looking for new destinations of natural beauty to visit. The Hotel Union Øye on Hjørundfjord opens its doors ready for a demanding clientele. The hotel's guest book reveals how the status of the hotel and the attractions of the area, gained the attentions of the rich and regal. Queen Wilhelmina of Holland, Emperor Wilhelm II of Germany, King Oscar II, Queen Maud and King Haakon VII are just some of the distinguished visitors who found their way to the hotel.

Fast forward to 1989, and 100 years on, the hotel has been restored to its magnificent splendour, just as it did originally when it opened in 1891.

Selected as one the world's 12 most exciting and enchanting hotels in 1996, each room carries the name of one of the famous guests that have stayed here. Perhaps you're temped by Queen Beatrice or Kaiser Wilhelm II. Maybe Sir Arthur Conan Doyle or Karen Blixen will take your fancy.

Apart from comfortable four-poster beds and modern bathrooms, every guest room is different. You will not find telephones, TVs or radios in the rooms as they have been intentionally omitted. Everything you do at the Hotel Union Øye is not just a journey to magnificent scenery and an exciting destination, but also a journey back in time.

Perhaps best described as a romantic "Fjord Palace" in Swiss style. It is idyllically situated amid beautiful, untouched natural scenery, with rich freshwater and fjord fishing close by. With service and facilities that match their Royal patronage - and stunning scenery, Hotel Union Øye defined luxury for an era of aristocratic celebrity.

LOCATION AND ACTIVITIES

The Hotel Union Øye is located in a peaceful village on Hjørundfjord, nestled among the Sunmmøre Alps. The valley of Norangdal in which it lies, is often described as Norway's most beautiful valley.

"A journey back in time"

AS Hotel Union Øye
Norangsfjorden
Norway
www.GoUnusual.com/HotelUnionOye

• Breakfast provided
• Bar / Restaurant on site

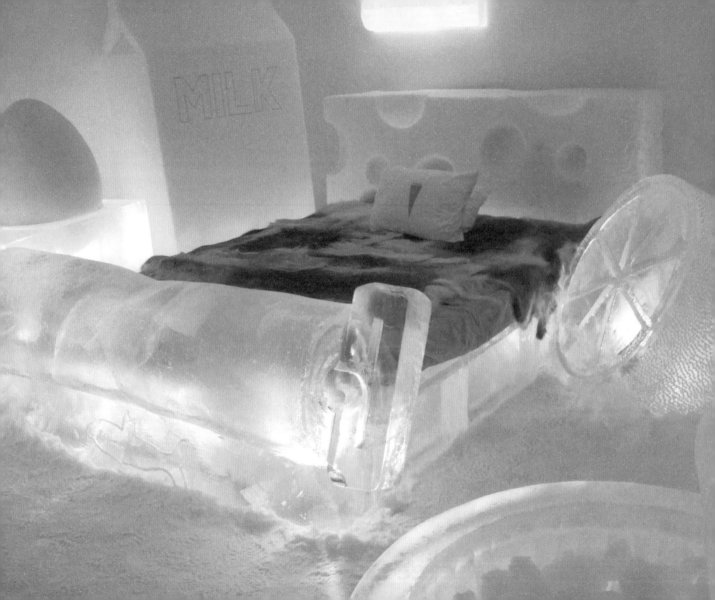

ICEHOTEL
THE ORIGINAL HOTEL MADE OF ICE

This is the original ICEHOTEL, first created in the early 1990's. It has become the global ambassador for this genre and now licenses ICEBARs around the world too. With 65 rooms and suites, the property is a huge undertaking to be rebuilt every year, and their expertise inspired other similar properties in North America and elsewhere.

The hotel offers the famous and indispensable ICEBAR JUKKASJÄRVI, open to non-residents, as well as an ice chapel sought out by couples as a venue to get married. Beware of drinking too much, as your trip to the (warm) bathroom requires a walk through the frozen corridors.

LOCATION AND ACTIVITIES

The ICEHOTEL offers two types of accommodation: standard bedrooms or Art suites. In both cases you sleep on a bed made of ice covered with an insulating sheet and reindeer skins. The ambient temperature is minus 5

degrees celsius - so it's chilly, but warmer than outside, where temperatures drop to minus 15 or more. Inside the room is a warm sleeping bag. Many guests keep on too many clothes in bed. They then get too hot, perspire, and spend the rest of the night in a cold, soggy sleeping bag.

Activities are worth booking early. You'll be disappointed if there aren't places on the husky adventure or skidoo trip if you leave it to the last minute.

"Be sure it is your partner you're cuddling. Everyone looks the same in a balaclava and jumpsuit!"

ICEHOTEL
Jukkasjärvi
Near Kiruna
98191
Sweden
www.GoUnusual.com/IceHotel

• Breakfast provided
• Bar / Restaurants on site

KAKSLAUTTANEN HOTEL AND IGLOO VILLAGE
WARM GLASS IGLOOS

Hotel Kakslauttanen is the home to unique glass igloos, as well as snow igloos and the world's largest snow restaurant. In addition guests can enjoy other Lappish winter activities including the Northern Lights - generally visible from late August to late April. Surrounded by Lapland's beautiful and stunning scenery, not only can guests sample the peace of sleeping in snow (the snow muffles sound, and provides a great night's sleep), their glass igloos are fantastic for lying on your bed at night, watching the Northern Lights in the warm.

LOCATION AND ACTIVITIES

The hotel offers 31 log cabins, 20 glass kota igloos and their igloo hotel rooms.

Overnight in a Snow Igloo:

Imagine you are sleeping in an Igloo made of Snow. It is totally quiet. Lights inside the ice illuminate the Igloo. These make the atmosphere so exciting that you'll never get bored, until you finally fall into a deep, comfortable sleep, in a warm, down-filled sleeping bag.

Overnight in a Glass Igloo:

When sleeping in a glass igloo, guests marvel at the millions of stars in the night sky and if they're lucky, see the amazing Northern Lights. The experience is particularly unforgettable when there is a snowstorm.

Kakslauttanen is a very good place to see the Northern Lights. With so few electric lights outside, there is nearly no light pollution and it is far enough North for the probability to be very high from late August to late April.

Igloo Village and Ice Gallery

In winter, from December until April, Hotel Kakslauttanen is near the famous Igloo Village where you'll discover 20 Snow Igloos, an Ice Gallery, Ice Bar, and an Ice Chapel - extremely popular for weddings.

"The Northern Lights from the warmth of your bed"

Kakslauttanen Hotel and Igloo Village
Kiilopääntie 9
Kakslauttanen, Saariselkä 99830
Finland
www.GoUnusual.com/KakslauttanenHotelandIglooVillage

"If you reject the food, ignore
the customs, fear the religion
and avoid the people, you might
better stay at home."

James Michener

Midnight

Sunset meets sunrise. Yesterday joins hands with tomorrow. Time stands still in the magic of the summer night.

VisitFinland.com

TREEHOTEL
TREEHOUSE RESORT

This stunning treetop accommodation in Harads in Northern Sweden was designed with the help of well known designers and architects, turning their ideas into unique treehouses, created in harmony with nature and their ecological values.

The Treehotel is open all year round, which means guests will be able to benefit from either the lovely hot summer or beautiful winter. To make this possible, each Treehotel has an electric under-floor heating system from an eco-friendly source of electricity.

All of the Treehouses are situated in pine trees between 4-6 meters from the ground. The rooms can be accessed by either a ramp or sturdy stairs. One of the rooms, Birds nest, has an electric, retractable stepladder.

They each have their own living and sleeping areas with between 2 and 4 beds as well as a state of the art eco-friendly incineration toilet and water efficient hand basin, which means there is no artificial plumbing. In addition there is a sauna and a relaxing area room seating 12 guests comfortably.

LOCATION AND ACTIVITIES

- Perhaps an action-packed dog sled ride through the frozen landscape, or perhaps the calm and quiet of a snow shoe walk in pursuit of the Northern lights?

Treehotel is located in the beautiful village of Harads, in the Norrbotten region of Northern Sweden, approx 80 km (1hr by car) from Luleå airport, (the largest airport in Northern Sweden), 47 km upstream from Boden. It is approximately 60 km south of the Arctic Circle.

With a population of around 600, Harads has restaurants, stores, a hostel, gas station, swimming facilities, viewing areas, as well as a beautiful church.

"A special experience, staying close to nature, in an area of natural beauty"

TreeHotel
Edeforsvägen 2A
960 24 Harads
Sweden
www.GoUnusual.com/Treehotel

• Bed & Breakfast
• Dinner by arrangement

KOLARBYN ECO-LODGE
CHARCOAL WORKER HUTS IN THE WOODS

Kolarbyn consists of twelve little forest huts located by the beautiful lake Skärsjön. Called Sweden s most primitive hotel, the huts have no electricity and the dark evenings are lit by candles or traditional oil lamps. Staying here is fantastic! There are blueberry bushes all around the site, so in summer you can pick the berries for your morning pancakes!

Each tiny hut provides two berths with sheepskin rugs to cushion your slumber. You are kept warm by a wood fire, with your first task to gather and chop adequate wood for your cooking and heating needs. During the week guests bring food to cook themselves at one of several fire places - one even has a view over lake Skärsjön.

The nearest supermarket is in Skinnskatteberg 3 kilometers away - open 7/7 from 0800 - 2000. A limited stock of pans and cutlery is available in the storehouse, but we recommend you bring your own plates and cutlery. You're cooking on an open fire, so should either plan to barbecue/grill, or use one of the supplied pans. There are a couple of big kettles for hot water and making tea/coffee.

There is also a sauna to chop wood for, though as washing facilities are limited to a stream, you are encouraged to be brave enough to cool down with a dip in the nearby lake.

The toilet is in a natural outhouse, which though rustic, serves its purpose adequately, as was the normal practice for centuries! It has been decorated into a 'royal privy' and provides clean, candle-lit peace.

Pack warm clothing for cool evenings - and be prepared for a fantastic camping experience.

LOCATION AND ACTIVITIES

Kolarbyn is a couple of hours by car from Stockholm and 60 minutes from Västerås. Alternatively trains run hourly from Stockholm Central Station to Köping where a connecting public bus runs to Skinnskatteberg for an arranged pick up by the Kolarbyn team.

"Fantastic to experience rustic charm with children!"

Kolarbyn Eco-Lodge
SKÄRSJÖN
Skinnskatteberg
Västerås
Sweden
www.GoUnusual.com/Kolarbyn

- Vacation Rental
- Min stay requirements
- Limited cooking facilities

WOODPECKER HOTEL
TREEHOUSE IN A CITY CENTRE LOCATION

Thirteen metres is a long way up any tree, let alone a 130 year oak tree in the central park of Västerås near Stockholm, Sweden. The Woodpecker hotel is another extraordinary brainchild of Mikael Genberg, artist and innovator of this hotel and its sister, the underwater Utter (Otter) Inn on nearby lake Mälaren.

Reached via a sturdy, but wobbly rope ladder, the platform has an impressive view of the park below and out to the lake beyond. Advice to "Pack light" was appreciated as your luggage is hoisted up on a rope from the treehouse platform.

On arrival you discover your picnic supper and breakfast packs await. There is a briefest of tours covering safety and operation of the most essential item at the top of a tree – a toilet. Pull up the rope ladder and you retire to find the treehouse well thought out and equipped. From an IKEA bed and duvet, heater and cooking facilities, Mikael has thought out your needs. There are even a few books in a small library, with a small lantern.

Surprisingly you never quite escape the background noise of the city centre but the rustle of leaves and sound of children playing football below is rather calming. Your mind finds peace when you're sitting quietly in a tree, though not enough to appreciate birdsong from the crack of dawn. It is surprising how loud birds are when you're at their level!

At night, the only reminder of civilization is the faint roar of traffic on the road far below. If you really want peace and solitude however, don't forget to turn off your mobile - coverage is rather good from this treetop vantage point.

LOCATION AND ACTIVITIES

Västerås is a thriving town about 40 minutes by train from central Stockholm, or 10 minutes from the low cost flight airport of Västerås. Restaurants and bars are within a 5 minute walk of the park. Most guests climb up the tree and stay there until the following morning, using the provided dinner package. The hotel opens at the beginning of April and the season runs through to late September.

"Sleep surrounded by trees"

Hotel Hackspett
Vasaparken in central Västerås
Västerås
Sweden
www.GoUnusual.com/WoodpeckerHotel

• Bed & Breakfast
• Dinner by arrangement

SALA SILVERMINE
WORLD'S DEEPEST BEDROOM UNDERGROUND

You can sleep 155 metres underground in an underground suite in historic Sala Silvermine, one of the world's best preserved mine settings. Here you will see dark winding galleries and vast caverns. Even to those not familiar with mining, the underground setting is sensational. It is cold, damp and dark, but very beautiful.

After a guided tour of the -155m underground level, you are provided with a basket of refreshments and something to drink. The guide then leaves you alone in your suite below ground to enjoy the refreshments and the solitude of the mine. In the morning a guide comes to serve your breakfast before you're taken to ground level again.

Wear warm and comfortable clothes for the underground tours. Year-round, it is only 2 degrees Celsius. The underground festivity hall and suite are warmed up to 18 degrees and the bed is equipped with a thick cover and an extra pair of blankets. A simple toilet is available about 50m away from the suite. Showers are available in the Sala Bed and Breakfast above ground.

The mine staff are available for you above ground during the whole night. You will be given an intercom radio through which you can communicate. Mobile phones do not work at 155 underground, so if you expect to be contacted, please ask them to ring the mine's general phone number.

LOCATION AND ACTIVITIES

Sala Silvermine is situated in the middle of Sweden in the Regional district of Västmanland. It is 120 kilometres from Stockholm, 62 kilometres from Uppsala, 37 kilometres from Västerås, 81 kilometres from Eskilstuna and 114 kilometres from Falun.

Experienced guides tell you of a fantastic chapter in industrial history. During its heyday, production amounted to more than 3 tons of silver a year, and a total of more than 400 tons of silver and about 40,000 tons of lead were extracted - completely by hand!

"Celebrate in a world of silver!"

Sala Silvermine Underground suite
Drottning Christinas väg
Sala
Västmanland
Sweden
www.GoUnusual.com/SalaSilvermineUndergroundsuite

• One suite only
• Refreshment basket included
• More facilities on surface

UTTER INN

FLOATING, UNDERWATER HOTEL, WHERE YOU SLEEP IN AN AQUARIUM

LOCATION AND ACTIVITIES

Västerås has direct flights from Stansted in the UK and the hotel is a 10 minute taxi ride from the airport to the docks. The town itself is very pleasant and has plenty of shops and restaurants worthy of a weekend visit.

Västerås is under an hour from central Stockholm, where you can connect to the train from the main airport of Arlanda.

"An aquarium - for fish to be beholders of man"

The single room of the Utter (Underwater) Inn lies 3m below the surface of Lake Mälaren in Västerås and contains only twin beds and a table. With panoramic windows in all directions it is the brainchild of Mikael Genberg, a local artist and sculptor. Opening in June 2000, the Utter Inn offers the most typical of Swedish dreams; to have a small Swedish red house with white garbles on your own island.

Guests arrive at the port of Västerås and they are taken 1 km out to the hotel on the Lake Mälaren by a small powerboat. Depending on their booking options, they're provided with a food hamper and an inflatable boat to visit the closest uninhabited island. Some guests sunbathe upstairs, while others watch the fish enjoying the seclusion and solitude.

Hugely popular, you need to book far ahead for availability.

Utter Inn
Västeråsfjärden 1 km out on Lake Mälaren
Västerås
Sweden
www.GoUnusual.com/UtterInn

• Bed & Breakfast
• Dinner by arrangement

JUMBO STAY
SLEEP IN A 747 JUMBO JET

This is a real c1976 Jumbo Jet, retired and converted to provide accommodation. Choose between a couple of en-suite rooms, budget dormitory, twin and three-bed combo rooms with shared shower and toilet in the corridor or the luxury suite in the cockpit with its panoramic view of the airport. At Jumbo Stay you're guaranteed a unique and outstanding experience for all traveler budgets.

LOCATION AND ACTIVITIES

You can hardly stay closer to the airport! Jumbo Stay is only a ten minute walk away from the check-in counters at Arlanda. Perfect for anyone catching an early flight who doesn't want to get out of bed before dawn to make it to the airport in time.

Start your trip in style with this alternative excursion for the family, and for anyone interested in airplanes. It certainly beats sitting in the lounge at Arlanda waiting for relatives to arrive!

Café: You don't even have to stay at the hostel to visit for a coffee or a snack in the café. You can buy breakfast, coffee, cookies and basic meals.

Parking: Café and day visitors have 10 parking places right next to the airplane. For guests that will travel away for more than one night they recommend long-term parking ALFA only 500 meters from Jumbo Stay. ALFA long-term parking is connected via the shuttle bus nr. 14 and passes Jumbo Stay on its way to the terminals.

Check out the Jumbo Suite Conference Facilities:

The first class lounge on the upper deck has been converted to provide a funky conference location for up to 8 people. Perfect for small business meetings with a difference!

"Scared of flying? Start your trip here!"

Jumbo Stay
Jumbovägen 4
Arlanda, Near Stockholm
Sweden
www.GoUnusual.com/JumboStay

• Bed & Breakfast
• Restaurant nearby

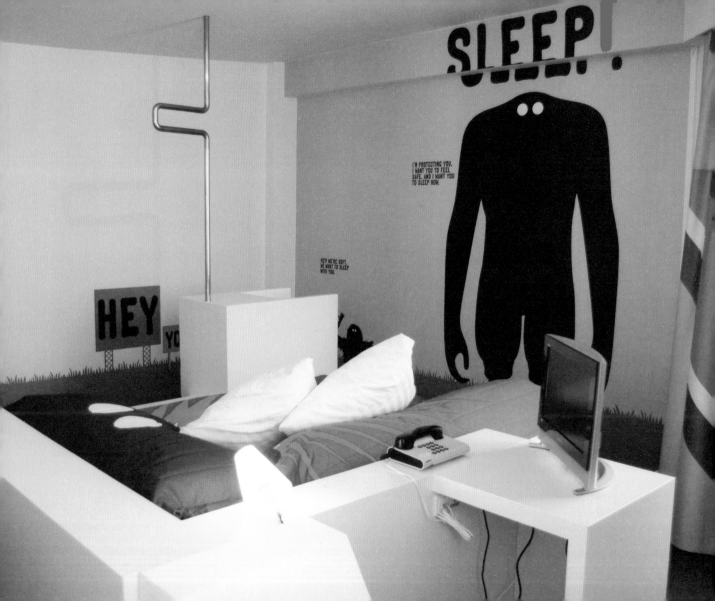

HOTEL FOX
CREATIVE FREEDOM IN COPENHAGEN

21 young international artists from different scenes – graphics, illustrations and arts – have decorated the hotel's 61 rooms. They had 100 percent artistic license to do so. And the result of their creativity must be experienced with all of your senses.

The artists either had multi-functional furniture specially designed - which elegantly and efficiently combines sitting arrangements with work-stations and TV, while at the same being a wardrobe. Or they opted for special, by way of example, vintage furniture and accessories. All rooms are equipped with flat-screen TV's for which their sizes are balanced against the respective rooms and a portable computer may be connected for enhanced audio-visual experiences.

It might be quite difficult to choose one room over another. To help, the hotel offers the possibility of going on a "tour de Fox" where you can try different rooms each night during a three-day stay. You really get to feel the different atmospheres, thoughts and dreams evoked in you by the artists' decorations.

LOCATION AND ACTIVITIES

Hotel Fox is situated in the heart of Copenhagen, right next to the City Hall Square "Rådhuspladsen", and in the midst of the pulsating Latin Quarter "Pisserenden", which is the trendy home of many artists, musicians, interesting restaurants, bars and fashionable cafés. The district is also known for its design shops and vintage boutiques, art galleries and music shops. So if you are on the lookout for second hand outfits or an old vinyl records, "Pisserenden" is the place to be.

"Art Gone Wild. It's a lot of fun!"

Hotel Fox
Jarmers Plads 3
Copenhagen DK-1551
Denmark
www.GoUnusual.com/HotelFox

Europe
United Kingdom and Ireland

Key
Entries in **Bold** typeface indicate full page entries with a photo.
Others are additional indexed entries.

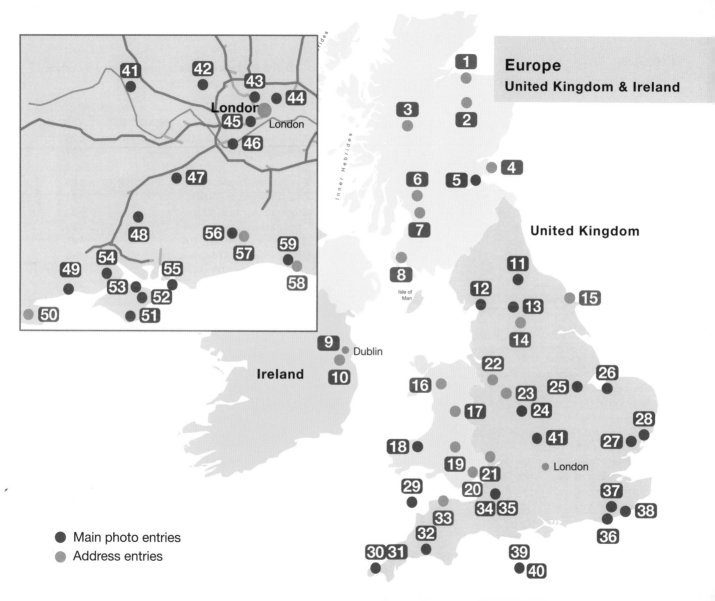

THE PINEAPPLE
FLAMBOYANCE AND EXTRAVAGANCE IN A COUNTRY SETTING

The Pineapple is an elaborate summerhouse of two storeys, built for the 4th Earl of Dunmore. Though classical and orthodox at ground level, it grows slowly into something entirely vegetable; conventional architraves put out shoots and end as prickly leaves of stone. It is an eccentric work, of undoubted genius, built of the very finest masonry. It probably began as a pavilion of one storey, dated 1761, and only grew its fruity dome after 1777, when Lord Dunmore was brought back, forcibly, from serving as Governor of Virginia. There, sailors would put a pineapple on the gatepost to announce their return home. Lord Dunmore, who was fond of a joke, announced his return more prominently.

The Pineapple presides over an immense walled garden. This, in the Scottish tradition, was built some distance from the house, to take advantage of a south-facing slope. To house the gardeners, stone bothies were built on either side of the Pineapple. These make plain, unassuming rooms to stay in, though you have to go out of doors to get from one part to the other.

The Pineapple and its surroundings are owned by the National Trust for Scotland. The Landmark Trust took on the lease in 1973 and restored all the buildings and the walled garden, now open to the public. There is a double and twin room in one wing of the property as well as the bathroom. Walking outside, you can then connect with a lounge and kitchen in the other wing. At the back, where the ground level is higher, there is a private garden for guests, with steps leading into the elegant room inside the Pineapple itself.

LOCATION AND ACTIVITIES

Between Falkirk and Stirling, near Kincardine bridge and Airth Castle. Locally a major attraction is the Falkirk Wheel - a modern architectural marvel that connects two different height stretches of canal via a giant counterbalanced wheel. Open year round, it is an impressive feat of engineering to see in action. Further away, but by no means far, is the ancient city of Stirling with its impressive castle.

"Hooray for the Pineapple, prickly and proud!"

The Pineapple
Dunmore, Central Scotland
c/o The Landmark Trust
United Kingdom
www.GoUnusual.com/ThePineapple

- Vacation Rental
- Min stay 3 nights
- Suitable for Groups
- Self catering facilities

CULLODEN TOWER
FLAMBOYANCE AND EXTRAVAGANCE IN A COUNTRY SETTING

Standing in splendid isolation looking down on Richmond, the tower was built by John Yorke, MP for Richmond, in 1746 to mark the Duke of Cumberland's defeat of Bonny Prince Charlie. It stands in the park of his long-demolished house, at the edge of a steep slope above the River Swale a few hundred yards away from the town.

Giant windows flood light in the tall octagonal rooms. A twin bedroom and bathroom are on the ground floor leading you to spiral staircase which rises to the mezzanine where the kitchen and dining area are located. Taking the stairs once again, you rise to the first (lounge area) and second floor bedroom. Keen eyes will note that the carving and plaster work style changes from Gothic below to Classical in the upper floors. On the second floor you sleep under what must be one of the grandest bedroom ceilings, worth all the 60 steps you have climbed to reach it. These steps are rather more tiresome if you're caught short in the night and need to visit the bathroom on the ground floor.

LOCATION AND ACTIVITIES

With a double and twin bedroom there is space enough for 4. As with many outstanding monuments such as this, a walk from the parking to your room is expected. A top visitor tip is to keep the doors closed to prevent any heat you've coaxed from the stove shooting up the stairway and out of the roof.

On the northern edge of Yorkshire Dales National Park, Richmond enjoys year-round tourism. Closest rail access is to Darlington.

It is difficult to imagine a more idyllic situation, enjoying lovely views from the big windows all around, looking over the trees of this park, with the sight and sound of the Swale hurrying over its rocks and stones below. With luck you'll have fine weather and chilled wine as the roof platform is ideal for an early evening view of the surrounding parkland with a glass of wine.

Richmond is a decent market town, with a good weekend market and shops for supplies and treats.

"To have a whole Tower to ourselves – along with an unexpected and amazing roof – was perfect!"

Culloden Tower
Richmond, North Yorkshire
c/o The Landmark Trust
United Kingdom
www.GoUnusual.com/CullodenTower

• Vacation Rental
• Min stay 3 nights
• Suitable for Groups
• Self catering facilities

THE MUSIC ROOM

MORE INTRICATE BAROQUE PLASTERWORK THAN IN ANY MUSEUM

Squashed into a little back alley behind The Sun hotel, this 1730's building was originally a summer house in the gardens of the hotel. Restoration was a huge undertaking, as access was near impossible and The Landmark Trust needed to buy the buildings on all sides and demolish them to give builders access to The Music Room itself. Such great efforts also necessitated the creation of a pedestrian square to preserve the striking façade and the glazing of the central Ionic arch to create a rather good ground floor café.

Once you've climbed to the music room inside you suddenly appreciate what an exceptional property this is, as the baroque plasterwork is hugely ornate and would not be out of place in a royal palace. On the walls are the muses: eloquence, history, music, astronomy, tragedy, rhetoric, dancing, comedy and amorous poetry; with Apollo over the fireplace. A fruitful goddess with a torch presides over the ceiling. One muse had vanished entirely and was recreated as a modern girl, big and busty, with a cheerful eye; she makes an excellent muse of dancing.

There is a double in the music room and a smaller twin on the 2nd floor in the attic above, reached by a narrow stair. From it and from the small terrace on its roof there are distant views over Lancaster.

LOCATION AND ACTIVITIES

Tucked away in the centre of Lancaster, a parking space is provided for a single car. Lancaster is a charming town, with many tucked away shops including some great traditional places like an old sweet shop (specialising in humbugs) www.humbugsuk.co.uk and a traditional coffee shop (not a café), J Atkinson & Co founded in 1837, that sells a huge variety of custom blends, and roasts their beans daily. They also run tours in August and September.

"A fine view of the Castle from the sink !"

The Music Room
Sun Street, Lancaster
c/o The Landmark Trust
United Kingdom
www.GoUnusual.com/TheMusicRoom

- Vacation Rental
- Min stay 3 nights
- Suitable for Groups
- Self catering facilities

BEAMSLEY HOSPITAL
CIRCULAR ALMSHOUSE

Almshouses were once a familiar part of our towns and villages, providing subsidized accommodation to the poor and needy through charitable endowments. Most were nondescript properties providing basic facilities, but the Hospital at Beamsley is more unusual. Originally providing accommodation for sick nuns in the 14th century, this circular stone building is set back from the conventional row of dwellings on the main road. Contained within were rooms for seven women, encircling a chapel, through which most of them had to pass to reach their doors, a daily encouragement to piety. Until the 1970s the little community of Mother and Sisters lived here, their lives governed by ancient, and ferociously strict, rules.

The Hospital was founded in 1593 by the Countess of Cumberland, at a time when the poor had only private charity to depend on. Her building is an Elizabethan conceit, alluding both to the six circles, or annulets, on her husband's coat of arms and to the round churches of the Templars. Her daughter, the formidable northern heroine Lady Anne Clifford, added the front range. She also furnished the chapel and, almshouses being of their nature conservative places, these fittings survive. Finding the buildings no longer in demand – perhaps as much because of the strict rules as because of the changing social fabric of society, the Trustees offered the property to The Landmark Trust. Providing a double, twin and single room there is accommodation for 5, and should you wish, well behaved dogs.

LOCATION AND ACTIVITIES

The nearest town is Bolton Bridge and the property is a short walk from the A59, set back from the main road. All around are the Yorkshire dales at their most unadulterated, with walks straight from the back door to stunning countryside year-round.

"So near to so many places to see we could have stayed here for a month "

Beamsley Hospital
Near Skipton, North Yorkshire
c/o The Landmark Trust
United Kingdom
www.GoUnusual.com/BeamsleyHospital

- Vacation Rental
- Min stay 3 nights
- Suitable for Groups
- Self catering facilities

"Life should not be a journey to the grave with the intention of arriving safely in a pretty and well preserved body, but rather to skid in broadside in a cloud of smoke, thoroughly used up, totally worn out, and loudly proclaiming "Wow! What a Ride!"

Hunter S. Thompson

"WENDY" THE ABERPORTH EXPRESS
RAILWAY CARRIAGE

LOCATION AND ACTIVITIES

Permission to build a permanent structure in this location would never be granted, so the opportunity to stay in something with its own history while you enjoy the view is particularly pleasing.

There are two insulated and oak-lined double bedrooms with proper sprung mattresses and a single children's bed, allowing you to sleep in comfort all year round. A modern kitchen and bathroom complete the rental package.

This is a peaceful location with no roads within 300 yards, and no neighbours or noise pollution.

"Pub, shop, chinese takeaway and cafe nearby"

This former Great Western Railway sleeping carriage has been relocated alongside a foot path in Wales with Panoramic views of the Ceredigion Heritage Coast. Called Wendy after the character in Peter Pan, it travelled the length and breadth of the Great Western line between England and Wales until it was retired in 1937.

Wendy
c/o Under the Thatch
Llandysul
Ceredigion Wales SA44 5UA
United Kingdom
www.GoUnusual.com/Wendy-TheAberporthExpress

CLOVER CLOTHES FREE SPA AND HOTEL
UK'S FIRST PRESTIGE CLOTHES FREE PROPERTY

LOCATION AND ACTIVITIES

Birmingham city centre has shops restaurants and all the nightlife you could wish for.

The NEC, NIA, Symphony hall and museums are all close by.

"Both regular visitors and first time guests find it a most relaxing, liberating and respectful place to be."

Unique to the UK, a high quality clothes free lifestyle spa and 7 bedroom hotel. With excellent hot tub, sauna and hamam facilities and a secluded garden to invigorate your senses and clear your mind.

The beds are all individually pocket sprung, the duvets and pillows are Hungarian down, all of which adds up to a wonderfully comfortable night's sleep.

En-suite wet rooms are luxurious, with heated floors, complimentary robes, slippers and toiletries. Each room also has a flat screen television, Wi-Fi access, hairdryer and hospitality tray.

Clover Clothes Free Spa and Hotel
Chester Road, Erdington
Birmingham, B24 0BY
United Kingdom
www.GoUnusual.com/CloverClothesFreeSpaandHotel

THE HOUSE OF CORRECTION
18TH CENTURY FORMER PRISON

The House of Correction occupies the site of a medieval castle where once the moat and earthworks where sited. Planned as a local prison, it was originally intended for minor offenders – the idle (regarded as subversive) and the disorderly. Folkingham had a house of correction by 1611, replaced in 1808 by a new one built inside the castle moat and intended to serve the whole of Kesteven. This was enlarged in 1825 and given a grand new entrance. In 1878 the prison was closed and the inner buildings converted into ten dwellings, all demolished in 1955.

The grand entrance alone survives. It was designed by Bryan Browning, an original and scholarly Lincolnshire architect also responsible for the Sessions House at Bourne. It is a bold and monumental work, intended to house the turnkey, and the Governor's horses and carriage. Now it gives entrance only to a moated expanse of grass – a noble piece of architecture in a beautiful and interesting place.

Accommodation is for up to 4 people, although you might find it a little snug around the dining table all at once. Keep your elbows to yourselves! In early and late season while the rooms are cosy enough, you might find the common areas a little chilly.

LOCATION AND ACTIVITIES

Folkingham is one of those agreeable places that are less important than they used to be. It has a single very wide street, lined on each side by handsome buildings, with a large eighteenth century inn across the top end. The property is a few minutes walk from the square, where there is a general store, pub and a couple of shops.

"Alas, parole came too early! An all too short sentence!"

The House of Correction
Folkingham, Lincolnshire
c/o The Landmark Trust
United Kingdom
www.GoUnusual.com/TheHouseofCorrection

- Vacation Rental
- Min stay 3 nights
- Suitable for Groups
- Self catering facilities

APPLETON WATER TOWER
WATER TOWER ON ROYAL ESTATE

A public-spirited local landowner offered The Landmark Trust the lease of this exceptional Victorian tower, who recognizing that there is seldom an opportunity to preserve a functional building such as this, let alone one of such quality, and mounted a successful appeal.

Designed by Robert Rawlinson, the foundation stone was laid in July 1877 by the Princess of Wales. The ground and first floors were the dwelling for the custodian, with a viewing room above reached by an outside stair. In a typically ingenious Victorian fashion, the flues from all the fireplaces passed through the centre of the iron tank to prevent the water from freezing – original, simple and practical.

The tower sleeps up to 4 people in 2 double rooms, There is a steep staircase so it is unsuitable for disabled guests or unsteady toddlers without close supervision.

The terrace on top of the tank is protected by an ornate cast-iron railing, and as from the room below, there is a view on all sides over miles of wide, open landscape. Here, on this exposed hilltop, you can even see a distant gleam of the Wash.

LOCATION AND ACTIVITIES

Apart from marveling at a view normally seen by birds, balloonists and pilots, the estate is an area of great wildlife diversity. The North Norfolk broads are within reach, as are shingle and sandy beaches. In winter, it can appear bleak – however a crackling fire and a good pub are a time honoured and satisfactory local remedy.

"The view from the top of the tower is marvellous and you can see for miles over fields and cottages"

Appleton Water Tower
Sandringham, Norfolk
c/o The Landmark Trust
United Kingdom
www.GoUnusual.com/AppletonWaterTower

- Vacation Rental
- Min stay 3 nights
- Suitable for Groups
- Self catering facilities

FRESTON TOWER
LOOKOUT TOWER OF UNKNOWN FUNCTION

No one really knows who built Freston tower or indeed why it was constructed. As yet the enigma of its existence points most closely to a wealthy Ipswich merchant called Thomas Gooding who bought the land of Freston Manor in 1553. Further records have yet to be unearthed and archive notes of the area are few. Its crisp brickwork and distinctive blue diapering however suggests that it was always intended to be an eye catching landmark – perhaps as a lookout tower for Gooding's ships, or simply as an extravagant folly – making it one of the first recorded examples. It may even have been built with royal favour in mind to coincide with Queen Elizabeth I progress to Ipswich in 1561.

Set in an old and undulating parkland of oaks, sweet chestnut, cedar and beech trees the architecture and construction is certainly exquisite. There are no fewer than 26 windows dotted over its six storeys, arranged in careful hierarchy. Intricate brick mullions and imitation stone window surrounds no doubt tested the craftsmen of the day – as they have done more recently for its renovation.

The kitchen is on the first floor, with bathroom above. For two storeys above are the bedrooms, a twin and double above, sleeping 4 in total. The sitting room then tops the tower on the fifth floor, to take advantage of unrivalled views of the River Orwell and its handsome modern bridge.

LOCATION AND ACTIVITIES

On the banks of the River Orwell outside Ipswich, facilities are few, but walking opportunities along the river and towards Pin Mill abound.

.

"We have enjoyed living vertically for a week – sad to be coming back down to earth"

Freston Tower
Near Ipswich, Suffolk
c/o The Landmark Trust
United Kingdom
www.GoUnusual.com/FrestonTower

• Vacation Rental
• Min stay 3 nights
• Suitable for Groups
• Self catering facilities

MARTELLO TOWER
NAPOLEONIC COASTAL FORTIFICATION

This is the largest and most northerly of the chain of fortified towers put up by the Board of Ordnance to keep out Napoleon. Built in the shape of a quatrefoil to house four heavy guns, nearly a million bricks were used in its construction. Although they successfully deterred the French from invasion, in this exposed position, the elements still attack. The installation of a purpose-made canopy over the main living space now provides significant protection with an agreeable nautical resonance of sails and canvas, however you should be prepared, during the rougher seas of winter, to expect that sometimes water will find its way inside.

Sensitively restored by the Landmark Trust after it was purchased in 1971, both exterior brickwork and the vaulted interior are maintained to the typical high standards of the Trust.

Choose your companions wisely as although the 2 bedrooms are screened from the central living area they are not fully divided. Lying in bed, the echoes from the oiled teak floors provide a sense of being in a larger loftier space – yet will hear your fellow guests as the acoustics are impressive.

LOCATION AND ACTIVITIES

Standing at the root of the Orford Ness peninsula, between the River Alde and the sea, it is only a few hundred yards from Aldeburgh. Many visitors bring sailing dinghies.

"We will remember the strange acoustics and the fishermen's lights along the beach"

Martello Tower
Aldeburgh, Suffolk
c/o The Landmark Trust
United Kingdom
www.GoUnusual.com/MartelloTower

• Vacation Rental
• Min stay 3 nights
• Suitable for Groups
• Self catering facilities

LUNDY

ISLAND WITH PRESERVED CASTLE, LIGHTHOUSE AND COTTAGES

Of the 23 houses and cottages, they include ones built around the keep of the castle, the keepers quarters of the lighthouse and a stone refuge without electricity – Tibbets, which has its own rustic charm.

LOCATION AND ACTIVITIES

Between March and November, The Landmark Trust run a ferry from Bideford or Ilfracombe carrying day and overnight visitors, weather permitting. Autumn and winter access is by helicopter from Hartland Point.

"An island retreat with stunning views"

Lundy ('Puffin Island'), in the approaches to the Bristol Channel, is three miles long and rises over 400 feet out of the sea, commanding a tremendous view of England, Wales and the Atlantic. It has tall cliffs towards the south and west, with grass and heather on top, and steep side lands with trees, shrubs and bracken in small hanging valleys, rich in wildflowers, on the east coast facing the mainland. There are three lighthouses (two in use), a castle, a church, farm, pub, several handsome houses and cottages.

Lundy offers the public a very rare experience. It is large enough to have a genuine life of its own, which visitors can share and enjoy, but small and far enough away to be a world apart and undefaced. All visitors have free run of the island. to sample both the pleasures of escape or participation. Looking east across the blue floor of the sea to the coast of Devon, or westward over the limitless Atlantic, sociable visits to the tavern and shop.

Lundy
Bristol Channel, Devon
c/o The Landmark Trust
United Kingdom
www.GoUnusual.com/LundyIsland

- Vacation Rental
- Min stay 3 nights
- Suitable for Groups
- Self catering facilities

ARTIST RESIDENCE - PENZANCE
COOL AND TRENDY

This boutique art property in the centre of Penzance, showcases the work of Cornish and British artists who have decorated individual rooms. Housed within a Grade II listed 17th Century Georgian mansion, (No.7 on the Penzance Town Trail), these 10 en-suite rooms have a funky, informal vibe – with top notch facilities.

Each of the playful 'sleep in a gallery' rooms has been individually designed - from wacky murals in the Jo Peel room, Pinky Vision pastel sea-scapes, butterfly themed Dolly Divine or cool & chic A.R Blank - where guests can create their own art by doodling on the blackboard walls. Some rooms have views to the sea over the rooftops. Others have beautiful original architectural features such as vaulted ceilings and large Georgian Windows. All are a delight.

Your private masterpiece has the comfort of quality bedding, modern en-suite shower rooms, flat screen digital TV's and eco-chic toiletries.

LOCATION AND ACTIVITIES

Located in the very centre of Penzance, just 5 minutes from the sparkling sea-front, ferry terminal and rail / bus station. Walk out of the chunky red front door and you are on Penzance's most vibrant street, crammed with cafe's, restaurants, shops and gallery's. Further afield, explore world famous attractions such as St Michaels Mount, the Minack Theatre and Lands End, as well as the South West Coastal Path for breathtaking walks. Popular towns, villages and beaches such as St Ives, Porthcurno, Mousehole and Sennen Cove are located close by.

"Sleep with your own private masterpiece"

Artist Residence - Penzance
20 Chapel Street
Penzance
Cornwall
United Kingdom
www.GoUnusual.com/ArtistResidencePenzance

• Bed & Breakfast

THE EGYPTIAN HOUSE
CELEBRATION OF NAPOLEONIC SUCCESS IN EGYPT

Of a style in vogue after Napoleon's campaign in Egypt of 1798, The Egyptian house dates from about 1835. The front elevation is very similar to that of the former Egyptian Hall in Piccadilly, designed in 1812 by P. F. Robinson. Robinson or Foulston of Plymouth are the most likely candidates for its design, though there is no evidence to support the claim of either. It was built for John Lavin as a museum and geological repository. Bought by The Landmark Trust in 1968, its colossal façade, with lotus bud capitals and enrichments of Coade stone, concealed two small granite houses above shops, solid and with a pleasant rear elevation, but very decrepit inside. These were reconstructed into three compact apartments, the highest of which has a view through a small window of Mounts Bay and St Michael's Mount, over the chimney pots of the city.

There are 3 apartments. The first floor with a narrow oval staircase to negotiate, accommodates up to 3. The second and third floors accommodate up to 4 people each in double and twin rooms.

LOCATION AND ACTIVITIES

Penzance itself is a handsome and lively town, easily accessible by train as well as by road.

"astonishing and eccentric"

The Egyptian House
Chapel Street, Penzance, Cornwall
c/o The Landmark Trust
United Kingdom
www.GoUnusual.com/TheEgyptianHouse

• Vacation Rental
• Min stay 3 nights
• Suitable for Groups
• Self catering facilities

RAILHOLIDAY
RESTORED RAILWAY CARRIAGES

Railholiday is a family company that has built a living providing self-catering accommodation in restored railway carriages. The family started with the restoration of The Old Luggage Van in 1995 and such was the demand that they added The Travelling Post Office to their St Germans station base. They have since added The St Ives Bay SK2 carriage at their second location in Hayle, about 5 miles from St Ives on the west coast of Cornwall. Railholiday's latest coach, a GWR slip coach called Mevagissey, will be available for families of up to five.

Each carriage has a different character, and perhaps the most historic is the 48 ft long Travelling Post Office No. 841, built for the Great Western Railway. It went into service in 1889, hauled by the City of Truro on its famous 100 mph run and was originally designed for broad gauge running. Converted to standard gauge in 1891 until its withdrawal in 1934, for many years the carriage formed part of a house in Wales. Now converted to sleep up to six in a combination of double room, sofa bed and bunk beds, The Travelling Post Office is a great place for families, friends and couples alike.

The passenger luggage van also has seen long service, having been built for the London and South Western Railway in 1896. It was recovered from a site at Wadebridge, Cornwall, in 1995 following its withdrawal from service in August 1932.

What the St Ives Bay carriage might lack in history (it was built in 1957), it makes up in original fittings, including all the compartments, lamp shades, luggage racks, mirrors, blinds and upholstery.

"St Germans and Hayle stations, Cornwall"

Railholiday Ltd.
Haparanda Station
Nut Tree Hill
St Germans
Cornwall PL12 5LU
United Kingdom
www.GoUnusual.com/Railholiday

• Vacation Rentals with min stay
• Suitable for Families
• Self catering facilities

BECKFORD'S TOWER
ARTISTIC TOWER FOLLY IN HISTORIC CITY LOCATION

Commissioned by William Beckford (1760–1844) this tower is designed in a Greek revival style, with a hint of Tuscany. Born immensely rich, Beckford became a collector, patron, writer and eccentric builder. Cold shouldered by English society, he became a recluse and bought two adjacent houses in Lansdown Crescent in Bath, to pursue his fascination with towers.

Each morning, accompanied by his dwarf and pack of spaniels, Beckford would ride up to his Tower to play with his treasures in its opulent rooms, described in the books of the tower museum, on display in the museum on the first floor.

After Beckford's death the Tower became a chapel and its grounds an elegant cemetery. Now returned to it's former glory, the ground floor of the property has been restored to recreate the layout and something of the flavour of Beckford's interiors, especially in the sumptuous Scarlet Drawing Room. Like him, those who stay here can climb the fine circular staircase to the 'Belvidere' just below the elaborate, gilded lantern and enjoy, all to themselves, what Beckford called 'the finest prospect in Europe'.

The tower accommodates up to 4 individuals in two bedrooms with a small garden and adjacent parking.

LOCATION AND ACTIVITIES

The museum and the Tower (but not the accommodation) are open to the public on weekends and Bank Holiday Mondays from 10.30–5.00pm between Easter and October.

"Beautifully presented building with a lot of magic"

Beckford's Tower
Lansdown Road, Bath
c/o The Landmark Trust
United Kingdom
www.GoUnusual.com/BeckfordsTower

• Vacation Rental
• Suitable for Groups
• Self catering facilities
• Min stay 3 nights

"Your time is limited, so don't waste it living someone else's life. Don't be trapped by dogma – which is living with the results of other people's thinking. Don't let the noise of other's opinions drown out your own inner voice. And most important, have the courage to follow your heart and intuition. They somehow already know what you truly want to become. Everything else is secondary."

Steve Jobs

CRU HOUSEBOATS
CITY CENTRE CANAL BOATS

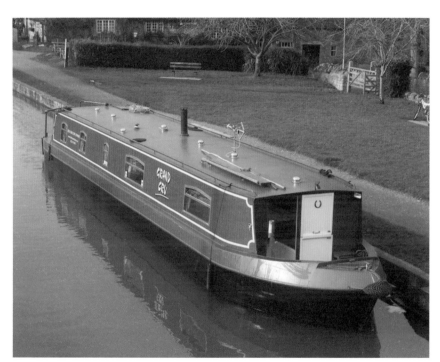

LOCATION AND ACTIVITIES

The price includes all the breakfast provisions and a cruise to a village pub. A car will collect/return you from Bath railway/coach station, or parking can be provided.

Everything is provided for you. Tea, fresh and instant coffee, milk, bacon, free range eggs, mushrooms, tomatoes, bread, croissants, butter, preserves, fruit juice and a selection of cereals and finally a bottle of chilled white wine ready for your arrival.

The minimum stay is two nights.

"Adventure afloat -
in the centre of Bath"

Moored just a 15 minute walk from the City of Bath, these "widebeam" canal boats are very comfortably furnished with full central heating, a cosy wood burner stove and a real brick fireplace. Sleeping four to six people in two double bed cabins and two single sofa beds, they're a fantastic alternative to families and small groups visiting Historic Bath.

Cru Houseboats
Sydney Gardens
Bath BA2 6NJ
United Kingdom
www.GoUnusual.com/CruHouseboats

"I never travel without my diary.
One should always have
something sensational to read in
the train."

Oscar Wilde

ELEPHANT LODGE
LUXURY CAMPING WITH A WILD TWIST

Offering two double beds, bunk and a sofa bed, there are plenty of bedroom options. Most importantly for the discerning glamper, there are private facilities attached to each luxury tent including showers with piping hot water.

LOCATION

Unlike so many campsites in the UK that are often just a gate into a grassed field of no significance, the Elephant Lodge tents are located at the top of the African elephant paddocks. Their commanding position means that they offer the most incredible uninterrupted views over the English Channel

"Glamping on the Wild side"

Elephant Lodge at Port Lympne is a unique and exciting short break, where families and friends can enjoy luxury camping with a wild twist. Consisting of ten glamping tents, sleeping up to 8 people, they offer unlimited free entry to explore 600 acres of both Port Lympne and Howletts Wild Animal Parks.

Tents have decked verandas, affording views over the cheetah and elephant paddocks to the Kent coast and beyond, perfect for relaxing with a cocktail and watching the sun set over the channel. Inside the tents, guests will find their living area with a cosy wood burning stove. During the summer, the sides of the tent can be fastened right back to make way for the perfect setting for an al fresco evening.

Port Lympne Wild Animal Park
Lympne Nr Ashford
Kent CT21 4PD
United Kingdom
www.GoUnusual.com/ElephantLodge

"I have found out that there ain't no surer way to find out whether you like people or hate them, than to travel with them."

Mark Twain

LIVINGSTONE LODGE
OVERNIGHT SAFARI

endangered species including giraffe, black rhino, zebra, eland and more - all set against a backdrop of stunning views across the Kent coast to France.

LOCATION AND EXPERIENCE

Private balconies provide guests with an uninterrupted view over the watering hole to the Kent coast and beyond.

Dinner is a five course African inspired meal cooked on a fire pit in the spacious and comfortable laapa accompanied by African wines, ciders and beers, finished with handmade chocolates.

"Wake up to the sounds of the Serengeti in Kent"

Voted the UK's Best Tourism Experience for three years in a row, Livingstone Lodge at Port Lympne Wild Animal Park, is the UK's first overnight safari lodge. Your 'out of Africa' night under the stars includes African fine dining and safaris guided by expert rangers, with firsthand knowledge of working on safari and wild animal reserves in Africa. The guided VIP safaris afford guests close views of animals roaming freely over The African Experience, 100 acres alive with some of Africa's most rare and

Livingstone Lodge
Lympne Nr Ashford
Kent CT21 4PD
United Kingdom
www.GoUnusual.com/LivingstoneLodge

BEACH SUN RETREAT
365 DAYS OF SUNSHINE IN BEACHSIDE RETREAT

Beach Sun Retreat uniquely offers the 'perfect beach and summer holiday' with guaranteed sunbathing 365 days a year! The retreat is one of the first in the country, alongside The Holistic Medical Centre in Harley Street and Grange St Pauls 5* Hotel, to have installed 'Real Sunlight's' innovative health-giving sun simulators, so you've got sunlight at the flick of a switch.

Occupying the ground floor of this former hotel, the property has been refurbished with two themed bedrooms to provide a stylish, one off and spacious holiday retreat, nestled in a quiet location at the end of a private road, with a large garden and direct access to the sandy beach.

It is a perfect venue for small parties, family holidays and romantic getaways.

LOCATION AND ACTIVITIES

There are 2 themed suites: "French" and "Bling" sleeping 4 comfortably and a single room.

The sun room is part of the St Tropez-style large living area and provides a multisensory tropical haven where guests can top up their tan and feel fabulous since it is beneficial against a whole host of health conditions such as SAD, stress, arthritis, skin problems, sleeping disorders, Vitamin D deficiency and so on.

Whether it is enjoying playing celebrity chef with the six-hob range cooker, spinning the high end vinyl decks as a superstar DJ, or relaxing in front of a great movie in the authentic cinema room featuring velvet cinema seats and

popcorn machine, guests will have a great time in this house!

For an excellent night's sleep, fully unwind in either the "French" or the "Bling" boutique style individually designed en-suite bedrooms featuring king size high quality beds, hand carved marble fireplaces, walk in showers/ Jacuzzi bath and sumptuous linen and towels.

"Bling bedroom and great beach 2 mins away"

Beach Sun Retreat
21 Sycamore Gardens,
Dymchurch,
Kent TN29 0LA
United Kingdom
www.GoUnusual.com/BeachSunRetreat

• Vacation rental
• Self catering options

FORT CLONQUE
18TH CENTURY FORTIFIED HARBOUR DEFENCES

In the 1840s it was thought that the advent of steam would make the Channel Islands more important as an advanced naval base, and also more liable to capture by the French. Accordingly the great harbour works of Alderney were begun in 1847. Fort Clonque, the most remarkable of them, occupies a group of large rocks off the steep south-west tip of the island, commanding the passage between it and the island of Burhou. The property is reached by a causeway leading to a drawbridge entrance and was originally designed for ten 64-pounder guns in four open batteries, manned by two officers and 50 men. Before the defensive capabilities of the base were fully realized, the further development of steam brought the Channel Islands within easy reach of mainland bases, and made a base in Alderney unnecessary. In 1886 the Defence Committee recommended that Clonque, and all the other works except Fort Albert, should be disarmed but left standing. It was thus that Hitler found them in 1940 and, imagining again that the Channel Islands had strategic value, vigorously refortified them. At Fort Clonque, part of the Victorian soldiers' quarters was replaced by an enormous casemate, housing a gun so large that its emplacement now makes a handsome bedroom looking towards Guernsey.

Most forts are large and grim, but Clonque was snugly fitted to the surrounding rocks, and is small, open and picturesque, ingeniously contrived on many levels to sleep up to 13 guests. The fort's location will sometimes make it cold and damp, however the compensation is the delight of its spectacular setting. Views are second to none; to the lighthouses of the Casquets; colonies of gannets and seabirds that fish around the fort; and of the formidable race or current called the Swinge, which runs between Clonque and Burhou.

LOCATION AND ACTIVITIES

Alderney benefits from clean air and fresh breezes and is a peaceful and extremely pleasant island, just small enough to be explored entirely on foot or, very easily, by bicycles which can be hired locally. The Victorian and German defence works are interesting, while the beaches at the north end are exceptional with plentiful, white sand. On calm days the sea can be heard all round the Clonque, restlessly searching the rocks; and on rough days it is comforting to reflect that the wall of the East Flank Battery is 19 feet thick. Stormy weather is no stranger to this location, and during some high tides the fort is cut off and the sea runs between it and the mainland.

"The fort is fantastic, especially during a good blow, when the sky rains sea foam!"

Fort Clonque
Alderney, Channel Islands
c/o The Landmark Trust
United Kingdom
www.GoUnusual.com/FortClonque

• Vacation Rental
• Min stay 3 nights
• Suitable for Groups
• Self catering facilities

Throw the lumber over, man! Let your boat of life be light, packed with only what you need – a homely home and simple pleasures, one or two friends, worth the name, someone to love and someone to love you, a cat, a dog, and a pipe or two, enough to eat and enough to wear, and a little more than enough to drink; for thirst is a dangerous thing.

Three Men in a Boat By Jerome K. Jerome

NICOLLE TOWER
NAVIGATION TOWER AND LOOKOUT

This 160 foot navigational mark is located in a field called Le Clos de Hercanty, where Hercanty means 'tilted menhir'. Used as a navigation mark, a small rectangular lookout was built next to the stone. In 1644, this half-buried slab of diorite was marked with a compass rose inscription to become part of the foundations of new lookout building, forming one corner. Records indicate that 18th Century owner Philippe Nicolle added the octagonal sitting room on the first floor in 1821. Further work was undertaken in 1943 by the occupying forces of the German army. They made an observation or control position here by astutely raising the roof of the octagon by a single storey so that no change would be noticed from the air. Although this latest addition with its slit eyes and German ranging marks on its thick concrete ceiling isn't part of the original tower, it has been renovated as part of the tower's history.

With a single bedroom for 2, this cosy landmark offers a unique perspective of the Island and surroundings. The staircase is necessarily steep without access for disabled guests. The tower also provides a garden should you tire of birds-eye views.

LOCATION AND ACTIVITIES

Set back from the coast, 160 feet up, the tower provides endlessly fascinating views over the sea and island in every direction.

"Peace, lovely walks, our own tower to live in – what more could you want?"

Nicolle Tower
St Clement's, Jersey
c/o The Landmark Trust
United Kingdom
www.GoUnusual.com/NicolleTower

- Vacation Rental
- Min stay 3 nights
- Suitable for Groups
- Self catering facilities

GOTHIC TEMPLE

TEMPLE FOLLY IN THE MANICURED LANDSCAPE GARDENS OF STOWE

Built in 1741, this James Gibb designed temple is dedicated "to the Liberty of our Ancestors", for which the Gothic style was deemed appropriate. Inside, the rooms are all circular, with moulded stone pilasters and plaster vaults – the main vault of the central space being gorgeously painted with heraldry. To be on the first floor gallery is an important architectural experience; and at the top of the staircase there is a belvedere with stone seats and a fine view over this former demesne of Lord Cobham and his successors, of which the National Trust is now guardian.

The ground floor provides a kitchen in the base of one tower, and modern bath and conveniences in the second. The centre is a lounge with a view of the valuated ceiling. Climbing the stairs enclosed in the third tower, you reach two double bedrooms - one in each tower, providing accommodation for four.

As might be expected in such a cavernous property, with high vaulted ceilings and solid stone walls, the effect of the heating system is slight – if any. Be prepared to wrap up well for early or late season breaks, or better still, ignore the temperature and just enjoy the amazing surroundings.

LOCATION AND ACTIVITIES

Stowe's majestic and famous gardens were designed by 'Capability' Brown and are recognized as one of the finest landscape gardens in the world.

"… we are spoiled for the future. Surely nowhere in Britain has a view like this"

Gothic Temple
Stowe, Buckinghamshire
c/o The Landmark Trust
United Kingdom
www.GoUnusual.com/GothicTemple

- Vacation Rental
- Min stay 3 nights
- Suitable for Groups
- Self catering facilities

CRAZY BEAR - BEACONSFIELD
LUXURY DESIGN AT ITS MOST DRAMATIC

The oldest documented building in Beaconsfield has been magnificently restored over four years in a made-to-order, without restraint, makeover. Its re-design can only be described as awesome – dramatic architecture, luxurious materials, spectacular lighting and even an underground extension create an elaborate, luxurious property. Each of the 17 individually designed bedrooms uses materials to dramatic effect. Textured leather, oak, porcelain, velvet and lots of gold leaf decorate rooms which are themselves filled with statement furniture and theatrical ornamentation.

The main bar is a work of art in its own right. From an Italian jade marble floor and gloss polished walnut & copper bar, to the two huge skylights where a row of six 1930s crystal chandeliers sit, you see top-to-toe luxury. Along one wall is a custom-made, seventeen metre black Chesterfield, studded with Swarovski crystals. A grand white marble staircase with an elaborate ironwork vine sculpture and python banister leads to the private bar, The Crystal Room. This underground Aladdins cave has mirrored walls, ceiling and fibre optic lighting effects. To complete the luxury of this property the garden has an infinity swimming pool and jacuzzi - kept at steaming hot temperature throughout the year.

The hotel has opened an Italian restaurant to complete a trio of delicious dining choices. Guests can enjoy the classic English restaurant featuring a huge open fire, crystal studded leather Chesterfield seating, 24 carat gold leaf walls and polished antique oak flooring. Alternatively there is a Thai restaurant, with embossed velvet walls, crystal chandeliers, leather tables and banquette seating.

All three have delicious food as dramatic as the setting!

LOCATION AND MEETING FACILITIES

On the main street in Old Beaconsfield, 2 minutes from M40 junction 2.

A number of meeting and private room facilities are provided, including The Library, which as well as a giant wall bookcase has a five and a half metre bird walnut boardroom dining table.

"Uninhibited and uncompromised design – a masterpiece"

Crazy Bear - Beaconsfield
Old Beaconsfield
Buckinghamshire
United Kingdom
www.GoUnusual.com/CrazyBear-Beaconsfield

• Breakfast provided
• Excellent Bar and Restaurants

CRAZY BEAR - STADHAMPTON
FLAMBOYANCE AND EXTRAVAGANCE IN A COUNTRY SETTING

The Crazy Bear is an oasis of eclectic style - extravagant design in a country setting. Reception is a lavishly re-styled double decker bus. The immediate gardens are tropical and abundant, paths lead past a waterfall through dense palm trees, terraces, lawns and woods – eye-catching art is scattered throughout the grounds.

The heart of the hotel is a sixteenth century building that has been bravely re-designed to house the bar and award winning restaurants. The vibrant bar is made up of traditional English architecture and outlandish extras including an 8 foot brown bear in the chandeliered gallery.

Seventeen bedrooms are spread throughout the establishment, each individually designed with amazing creativity and charisma – brave structures, elaborate furniture and luxurious materials create real wow-factor.

The Thai brasserie is a dramatic haven – steps lead down from the bar to a discreet room with real impact, there is a beautifully lit wine cellar to one side, mirrored ceiling, and faces that appear to be pushing through the velvet walls. Royal Thai cuisine is prepared by Thai chefs using produce from the hotel's farm and direct from Thailand. The English restaurant is bold and sumptuous – wine bottles form the ceiling, animal print covers the floor, and there's lots of padded leather, mirrors, chandeliers and impressive lighting. Modern British food is prepared using the freshest produce and meat that is home reared to specific menu requirements. Private dining, weddings and business meetings take place in a rich oak room (which has a civil marriage license), a garden log cabin and a huge Moroccan glasshouse.

LOCATION AND ACTIVITIES

The property is in Stadhampton, 20 minutes from the centre of Oxford. Set at the front of sixty acres of farmland, home to rare breed animals and The Crazy Bear Farm Shop which rears, butchers, cures and smokes it's own produce for the hotel and retail customers.

"A unique design offering a lot of fun"

Crazy Bear – Oxford
Bear Lane, Stadhampton
near Oxford, Oxfordshire
OX44 7UR
United Kingdom
www.GoUnusual.com/CrazyBear-Oxford

• Breakfast provided
• Excellent Bar and Restaurants

CLINK 78
MAGISTRATES COURT CONVERTED TO HOSTEL

This 200-year-old courthouse was originally used for petty criminal and less serious offences, although The Clash punk group were convicted here in the 70's.

Restored and converted to offer a combination of hostel dormitory, single and double rooms, as well as 6 original prison cells it's funky, up-beat and classy.

The prison cells can accommodate two, or be used for solitary confinement. This is the place where the accused used to stay before being brought before the judge. Perhaps a stag or hen party might sleep in a dormitory, with the cell room more appropriate for the bride or groom? The cells have been recently refurbished with an injection of colour, warmth and humour. English Heritage listed, they have kept many original features such as the heavy door; the barred-window and bench. The toilet is for decorative purposes only. If the cells sound too scary, there are plenty of other room alternatives from doubles to dormitorys sleeping up to 16. However, if you want to tell your friends that you slept a night in a cell in the Clink, some small sacrifice may be necessary!

LOCATION AND ACTIVITIES

Retaining the original facade and many of the courtroom relics, this Grade II listed building is situated in a conservation area 10 minutes walk from King's Cross station. It's a very interesting building and there are plenty of nooks and crannies to discover including details of famous names connected with it including Charles Dickens - who supposedly based parts of Oliver Twist on his experiences while working as a Scribe. As well as a self catering kitchen and Clash Bar with daily events, there is also an internet cafe in the old courtroom. There is also a staffed on-site discount Travelshop which can arrange tours, tickets and give advice on London things to do.

**"History on a Budget
- delivered with passion and attitude!"**

CLINK 78
78 Kings Cross Road
London WC1X 9QG
United Kingdom
www.GoUnusual.com/Clink78

• Hostel accommodation
• Bed & Breakfast

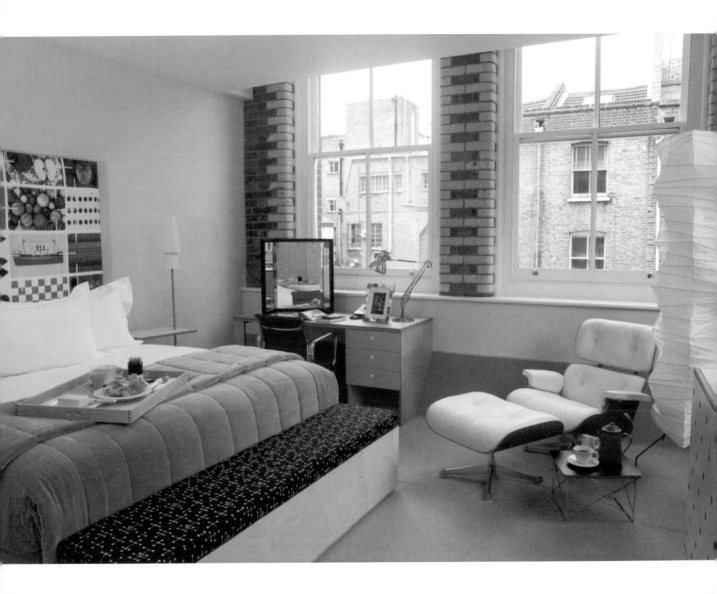

BOUNDARY
DESIGNER ROOMS IN VICTORIAN WAREHOUSE

Housed in a Victorian warehouse and former printing works, Boundary provides a high quality experience without gimmicks. Conceived from a love of the good things in life. Whether it's the selection of freshly baked breads in the morning at Albion or the studiously constructed selection of wines from their Master Sommelier, a warm summers evening spent on the rooftop with friends or a great nights sleep in one of the 17 individually designed bedrooms or suites, Boundary offers plenty to be happy about.

The rooftop is hugely popular in the summer months, when Londoners are lucky enough to have some sun. Guests can enjoy the balmy weather during the day and when the sun goes down there are warm blankets and a roaring fire if it becomes chilly. The line outside waiting to get to the rooftop can be easily circumvented. Just book into one of the rooms for the evening. Hotel guests always have priority.

Opened by Sir Terence Conran, Lady Vicki Conran and Peter Prescott on New Years Eve 2008, Boundary, it's restaurant, Albion cafe and rooftop bar are now firmly established members of the Shoreditch community.

LOCATION AND ACTIVITIES

Boundary restaurant offers classic French dishes using locally sourced British products and boasts one of the most impressive wine lists in London. Head chef, Frederick Forster, won the national chef of the year competition in 2011 and also won the Roux Scholarship.

Since opening, Albion has become a hub of the community in Shoreditch where locals sit communally with international visitors and enjoy traditional British fare while perhaps watching a fashion shoot on the street outside.

"I have always liked the idea of having a very good lunch or dinner, a cigar, coffee and digestive on the roof terrace, then to bed perhaps with a friend. This happens at Boundary I'm pleased to say."

- Sir Terence Conran

Boundary
2-4 Boundary Street
Shoreditch London E2 7DD
United Kingdom
www.GoUnusual.com/Boundary

153

THE PAVILION
FUNKY ROCK'N'ROLL HOTEL IN CENTRAL LONDON

The Pavilion Hotel is a small funky laid back townhouse in central London. Created by the brother and sister duo of Danny and Noshi Karne as an eclectic, exquisite alternative to boring hotels.

Danny is a former fashion model who got tired of staying in boring hotels around the world and wanted to set up something different.

All the 30 rooms have en-suite facilities and are decorated in a variety of amazing styles, from Honky Tonk Afro - as a tribute to the 70's through to Better Red Than Dead - a room covered in every imaginable shade of red. Popular for photo shoots and with actors, musicians and pop stars, it's regularly used for TV and Music video's.

Guests from supermodels to actors, actresses and musicians have included; Sophie Anderton, Naomi Campbell, Erin O'Connor, Helena Bonam Carter, Daniel Day Lewis, Antonia 'Huggy Bear' Fargas, Jools Holland and Bryan Ferry

Honky Tonk Afro: A humorous interpretation of the decade of unbounded excess that was the '70's. Walls are a vibrant lime green, boldly trimmed with fluorescent pink feather boas. Curtains are sequined in true disco style and tied back with furry dice. Heart shaped mirrored headboards are complemented by hippy glass beads in jewel colour draped around the twin beds. There is a disco ball (of course) and walls are adorned with pictures of icons from that era. There is no restraint. Kitsch, over the top and groovy.

Indian Summer: A quirky interpretation of the majestic splendour of a Maharajah's palace. This small but elegant room combines jewel shades with solid colonial furniture.

LOCATION AND ACTIVITIES
About 5 minutes walk from Edgware Road tube station, The Pavilion gives easy access to the sights of London.

"From 70s fab to rock'n'roll in Central London"

The Pavilion Hotel
Sussex Gardens
London
United Kingdom
www.GoUnusual.com/ThePavilion

• Bed & Breakfast
• Bar / Restaurants nearby

"When preparing to travel, lay out all your clothes and all your money. Then take half the clothes and twice the money."

Susan Heller

HAMPTON COURT PALACE

GRACE AND FAVOUR APARTMENTS IN HISTORIC ROYAL PALACE

Hampton Court Place is no empty museum and The Landmark Trust has been granted the opportunity to allow members of the public to stay in 2 properties on behalf of custodians, Historic Royal Palaces. The tradition of loyal servants of the crown being allowed to remain in royal apartments after completion of their service follows a precedent known as Grace and Favour set by George III.

The Palace itself needs little introduction. Visitors staying here get a sense of a secret life beyond the public eye - of doors leading up invisible corridors, of figures disappearing up a staircase with a shopping basket, of a life beyond the security barriers in one of the most loved of Henry VIII's palaces.

Fish Court is an apartment in the serving wing of the Tudor Palace, originally provided for the Officers of the Pastry and adjoined to the main palace. Famous for his lavish entertaining, Henry VIII commissioned many new kitchens including one entirely for the baking of pies.

The Georgian House used to be home to the Clerk of Works for the palace and was also originally a kitchen, built in 1719. It provides a private walled garden into which the morning sun shines and includes attic bedrooms that overlook of the beautiful palace roofs.

Fish Court has 4 bedrooms and sleeps up to 6, while The Georgian House accommodates up to 8 in a variety of single, double and twin rooms.

LOCATION AND ACTIVITIES

Guests are free to explore the gardens and most of the courtyards at all times, early and late, and the public rooms of the palace during opening hours. If you should ever tire of the amazing opportunities your access provides, London is only 35 minutes away by train and the River Thames is alongside, offering boat trips to Kingston and Richmond.

"We never dreamed we would be able to stay in Henry VIII's home. What a gracious host he was"

Hampton Court Palace
East Molesey, Surrey
c/o The Landmark Trust
United Kingdom
www.GoUnusual.com/HamptonCourtPalace

• Vacation Rental
• Min stay 3 nights
• Suitable for Groups
• Self catering facilities

MANOR FARM
FARMSTAY GLAMPING

The format of luxury tents with modern conveniences, offering accommodation for holidays on a working farm, has an enduring charm. Manor Farm near Alton was the first Feather Down Farm in the UK and continues to offer a fantastic back-to-nature glamping experience. With views of the rolling Hampshire countryside and the warmth of a wood fired stove, this is an amazing place for adults to relax. Equally, children, both young and old, will find plenty to keep them amused. Climbing trees, visiting the animals, farm tours are all part of the pleasure.

All Feather Down locations offer similar accommodation, based around a huge tent with raised wooden floor, open plan dining table and wood-fired stove - used for both cooking and warmth. Evenings are candle and oil lit, although you'll probably turn in early to compensate for the early start that fresh air encourages.

"Outdoor fun for everyone"

Feather Down Farm Days
Manor Farm
Alton
United Kingdom
www.GoUnusual.com/ManorFarm

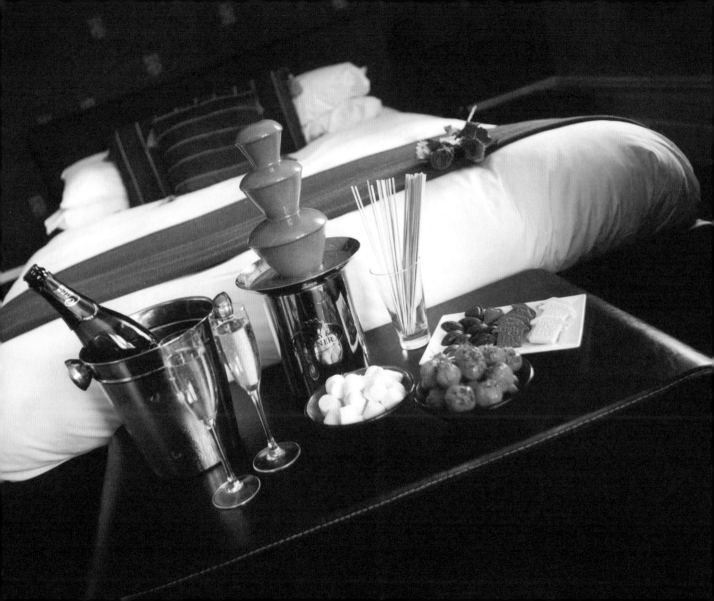

THE CHOCOLATE BOUTIQUE HOTEL
CHOCOLATE THEMED HOTEL

Whether you're a chocolate lover, want a romantic break or are simply looking for a chic hotel that is a little out of the ordinary, the Chocolate Boutique Hotel is the place to go.

LOCATION AND ACTIVITIES

Situated in West Cliff, near Bournemouth's fashionable Soho Quarter, the hotel is 5 minutes from Bournemouth's town centre and close to its award winning beaches

"Yum YUM !"

Once described as the perfect place to help mend a broken heart, Bournemouth's Chocolate Boutique Hotel is a chocolate lover's dream come true. Family run by Gerry and Roo Wilton, each of the 13 rooms in this Grade II listed property are chocolate themed, from the Maya to the Montezuma. Guests can sip decadent chocolate Martinis in the Chocolate Bar and dip fresh strawberries into cascading chocolate fountains available in rooms.

Learn about the fascinating history of chocolate and the culinary art of making delicious chocolate truffles at special Chocolate Delight workshops. You can even immortalise yourself or a friend in a chocolate portrait painting session, using melted milk, dark and white chocolate.

The hotel offers 2 scrumptious suites, 6 delicious doubles, 4 tantalising twins and the sweetest single, each with their own complimentary selection of divine handmade chocolates.

The Chocolate Boutique Hotel
5 Durley Road
Bournemouth
Dorset
United Kingdom
www.GoUnusual.com/TheChocolateBoutiqueHotel

• Bed & Breakfast
• Excellent Bar in hotel
• Restaurants nearby

GOTHIC VIEW
VICTORIAN CHAPEL

Gothic View is an Old Victorian Chapel with many original features. Set in rural countryside within easy reach of many beautiful beaches and local tourist attractions it is a fantastic base from which to explore the Island. Offering fresh and local produce, Gothic View combines the charm of an original chapel, with comfortable rooms and succulent gourmet meals which are lovingly prepared by Claude, jovial French Chef and husband of Anne Marie.

Each of the 3 rooms are cosy and comfortable, and there is parking on the road outside.

One is a family room which can be one double room with a connecting twin room with en-suite bathroom/shower WC.

The third room is a twin / double with attic style shower, WC and private patio.

Anne Marie and Claude are wonderful hosts, speaking both French and Italian. Whether you are staying for the night, or simply want to enjoy a special meal, you'll enjoy the rooms, food, and if wished, company - perhaps becoming one of their many regular visitors.

LOCATION AND ACTIVITIES

Lovely beaches are a short drive away, and the Isle of Wight retains its turn of the century Victorian charm, with a village feel to the Island. Families enjoy visits to the Blackgang Chine Adventure park, 5 minutes drive from Gothic View as well as nature walks to St Catherines Point and the Lighthouse.

Alternatively ask about the Gourmet meals cooked by Claude, including a starter, main course and desert. They don't have an alcohol licence to allow them to sell wine, so bring a bottle of your favourite. All ingredients are sourced fresh from around the Island, so please book in advance.

Claude takes a lot of pride in his cuisine - both for dinner and breakfast. Anne Marie equally takes great care to ensure that the rooms are warm and welcoming.

With decades of experience heading the kitchens of some of the most prestigious hotels and restaurants in the UK and France, Claude now enjoys serving his French inspired dishes in a homely atmosphere where guests become part of the family.

"Gourmet Alert!
Great food and hospitality at Gothic View"

Gothic View
Town Lane
Chale Green, Ventnor
Isle of Wight
United Kingdom
www.GoUnusual.com/GothicView

• Bed & Breakfast
• Gourmet Cookery

"When you travel, remember that a foreign country is not designed to make you comfortable. It is designed to make its own people comfortable."

Clifton Fadiman

ENCHANTED MANOR
FAIRYTALE PROPERTY FOR ROMANCE

LOCATION AND ACTIVITIES

The Enchanted Manor is located in its own private gardens and woodlands on the Isle of Wight. Nearby are some of the best walks on the Island with stunning scenery, breathtaking countryside and sea views. Within 10 minutes drive are the main coastal resorts of Shanklin and Ventnor and the Islands capital Newport. The Enchanted Manor is the ideal place for exploring the Island and is a gateway to the stunning coastal drive from Niton to Freshwater bay.

"Enchanted Wedding and
Celebration accommodation"

Ric and Maggie Hilton welcome you to their bed and breakfast, which they have restored into a celebrity celebrated magical retreat. Providing magnificent suites and opulent décor, most with ornate four poster beds and separate sumptuous lounge areas, it is a favourite for intimate weddings and receptions.

Winner of many Hospitality Awards as well as the Funkiest B&B in the UK.

Enchanted Manor
Sandrock Road
Niton Undercliff
Isle of Wight
United Kingdom
www.GoUnusual.com/TheEnchantedManor

VINTAGE VACATIONS
AIRSTREAM CARAVANS – RESTORED AND ADORED

Starting with a single Airstream caravan bought on eBay in 2004 as a weekend escape from London, owners Helen and Frazer saw the opportunity to offer these icons of travelling hospitality to others. Located on a working farm, the first of these 60's and 70s works of aluminium art were brought to the Isle of Wight from Missouri and enhanced with a treasure trove of furnishings from Helen's stylist background. Melamine plates and retro print fabrics, books and even cutlery - guests will be enthralled by the period artefacts chosen to make the Vintage Vacation experience a hazy trip down memory lane – full of a sense of period fun.

Modern conveniences such as fridges and CD players are hidden behind the vintage exteriors so you can enjoy yourself without sacrifice. They even include a hairdryer and toaster! Some of the larger models have enough space for travel cots. The campsite has a beach hut with proper toilet facilities as you can't use the toilets on board. Once inside your Airstream you'll easily understand why they are still considered king of the road for luxury camping.

Caravans sleep up to four, however vintage folding caravans are available to hire for noisy children or larger families.

To keep everything as original as possible, Vintage Vacations have stayed with the USA voltage. This means that each trailer has its own transformer to convert UK power supply to US. There is a travel adaptor on board. Most devices such as iPods, certain DVD players and phone chargers will work, but not all, so bring a couple of favourite CDs just in case.

LOCATION AND ACTIVITIES

The Isle of Wight offers all that is great about a traditional British beach holiday, with sunshine, ice cream sundaes, pony rides and pub grub. Top locations include Ventnor and Freshwater Bay with peaceful little coves, Shanklin for traditional teashops or Bembridge for safe bathing. Traditional board games (Cluedo, cards, etc.) are supplied. Newport is a 10 minute drive away.

To preserve these works of art, the caravans are non-smoking throughout and pets are not admitted on site.

"Retro luxury fun"

Vintage Vacations
Near Newport
Isle of Wight
United Kingdom
www.GoUnusual.com/VintageVacations

- Vacation Rental
- 2 night min stay
- Self catering
- Shop on site for essentials

LUTTRELLS TOWER

GEORGIAN TOWER WITH SMUGGLERS TUNNEL AND SOLENT VIEWS

a reputation locally as a smuggler, perhaps because of a tunnel made from the basement of the tower to the beach. The tower had several owners including for a time Marconi, who used it for his wireless experiments of 1912.

Purchased by The Landmark Trust in 1968 and restored to it's former splendour, all the rooms have handsome chimney pieces and the top room has fine plaster and shellwork as well. There is accommodation for up to 4 people in a double and twin bedroom combination. They have arranged this top room with an open plan kitchen so that you can cook, eat and sit in it, watching the Solent all the while.

LOCATION AND ACTIVITIES

With a roof terrace for summer months or al fresco breakfast, the real pleasure is to sit and watch. With the open spaces and walks of the New Forest nearby it is a splendid base from which to enjoy walks and country pubs. Even in winter, the clear skies and marvelous sunsets make this a magical location.

The view of the Solent towards Cowes from this Georgian folly, particularly of ships entering and leaving Southampton by the deep water channel is endlessly fascinating. Giant ships, sailing and pleasure craft of all shapes and sizes travel along this busy waterway and home of sailing. The view out of the opposite windows of the Fawley refinery and power station is in it's own way equally impressive, with miles of complex pipework knitted together in an intricate sculpture.

Built for Temple Luttrell, a Member of Parliament, he gained

"A beautiful and tranquil place"

Luttrells Tower
Eaglehurst, Southampton, Hampshire
c/o The Landmark Trust
United Kingdom
www.GoUnusual.com/LuttrellsTower

• Vacation Rental
• Min stay 3 nights
• Suitable for Groups
• Self catering facilities

SPITBANK FORT
LUXURY SOLENT FORT

Not only are the facilities luxurious, and interiors stunning, but the rooms offer views towards Portsmouth Harbour and Spinnaker Tower.

LOCATION AND ACTIVITIES

Outside there are barbecue facilities and a fire pit with the stunning views towards the Isle of Wight, perfect to watch the sun set over the Solent.

Within the basement of the Fort, rooms have been transformed to offer recreation facilities with everything from darts to bar billiards, a pinball machine to a poker table.

Stays include a 20 minute skippered ferry transfer from Gosport to the fort. Other locations, including trips to the Gunwharf Quay retail outlet can be arranged.

Spitbank Fort is an unusual and historic sea fortress in the Solent, off Portsmouth. Now a luxury exclusive venue and hotel, the fort was formerly home to hundreds of soldiers guarding the approaches to Portsmouth. The arms and ammunition have long been removed, making way for nine luxuriously furnished bedroom suites, three bars, hot pool, sauna and three restaurant areas including The Officer's Mess, which also offers a fantastic Sunday Lunch at Sea package.

"Defensive fortress, converted to a luxury private island and hotel"

Spitbank Fort
Royal Clarence Marina
Weevil Way, Gosport
Hampshire PO12 1FX
United Kingdom
www.GoUnusual.com/SpitbankFort

THE OLD RAILWAY STATION
PULLMAN CARRIAGES CONVERTED TO LUXURY SUITES

Luxury train journeys were once defined by Pullman train services such as the Orient Express, The Golden Arrow and Bournemouth Belle, and some of their Pullman carriages have been lovingly restored here.

There are four Pullman carriages providing 8 suites. Many elements have been improved, like fully equipped bathrooms, while others are simply retained, such as the splendor of the decorations.

In addition, the Old Station House, built in 1892 for the Prince of Wales - later Edward VII - has been sympathetically restored, providing two additional en-suite bedrooms.

LOCATION AND ACTIVITIES

It is not impossible to imagine yourself returning to the heyday of steam and The Old Station provides a perfect overnight stop if you are planning to participate in nearby themed events such as the historic Goodwood motor sport weekends. Anniversaries would have a touch of class here, especially if you choose to do the right thing and dress appropriately for the occasion as would have been required in a Pullman.

While there is no restaurant, breakfast is either served in the Station's Waiting Room, or on the platform in summer. A busy "gastropub" is next door, offering excellent food, while other pubs and restaurants are close by.

Petworth is handy for day trips to the south coast, including towns such as Arundel with its castle. Goodwood is also a short drive away, both for historic motorsport events and horse racing.

There is a minimum stay of two nights during weekends and it is worth checking availability for midweek breaks.

With a crackling log fire in the autumn and winter this is a year-round venue for special occasions and romantic weekends.

"Dress to impress in these classy carriages!"

The Old Railway Station
Station Road
Petworth, Near Chichester
West Sussex GU28 0JF
United Kingdom
www.GoUnusual.com/TheOldRailwayStation

• Bed & Breakfast
• Restaurant nearby
• 2 night minimum stay on weekends

ARTIST RESIDENCE - BRIGHTON
BE INSPIRED BY ART

This is a small, boutique style, art hotel in the centre of Brighton that showcases the work of well known artists. Each of the 14 bedrooms is decorated in styles from urban graffiti to cosy romance. Some have magnificent sea views over the West Pier and all will charm you with their sense of fun and frivolity

Artist Residence supports the local arts scene through its artist in residence scheme. They select one lucky artist and give them a room for 3 months with free rent and then hold an exhibition for them at the end of their stay.

All guests have access to the wi-fi cafe which has sea views and high ceilings, where you can enjoy the view with a nice cup of tea. Artist Residence's home cook Trish has put a lot of thought into food. You're able to enjoy a cooked or continental breakfast with great things on the menu, such as artisan bread and mushrooms with halloumi.

For those that need to work, each room has a desk and chair - or just find a cosy spot in the cafe, or on the beach!

The on-site art gallery is popular with locals holding monthly exhibitions. There is also an art café surrounded by screen prints for sale.

"Unpretentious, accessible art and a superb location"

LOCATION AND ACTIVITIES

Artist Residence Hotel is in the very centre of Brighton where many of the city's bars and shops are located. You are only 10 minutes from the North and South Laines as well as the usual historic places such as the Royal Pavilion and tourist attractions such the Brighton Palace Pier.

Artist Residence - Brighton
33 Regency Square
Brighton
East Sussex BN1 2GG
United Kingdom
www.GoUnusual.com/ArtistResidenceBrighton

• Bed & Breakfast

Europe

Belgium / Netherlands

Key

Entries in **Bold** typeface indicate full page entries with a photo.
Others are additional indexed entries.

Europe
Belgium / Netherlands

1
5
2
3
4
6
8
7
9
Amsterdam
10
11
13
15
14
12
16
Netherlands
17
19
18
Brussels
20
21
24
25
23
26
22
27

Belgium

● Main photo entries
● Address entries

CRANE HOTEL

DOCKSIDE CRANE CONVERTED INTO A SPINNING HIDEAWAY

This is a genuine dockside crane which has been the recipient of intelligent engineering and dedicated devotion rarely seen. Replacing the external ladders with modern lifts to gain entry, the old machine room in the body of the crane has been transformed into a luxurious bedroom that would not be out of place in the most modern of design hotels.

It is an out of this world property - staying here guarantees you stories to tell your friends!

The industrial feel of the crane has survived the renovation, but comfort, warmth, the latest flat screen TV and audio equipment has been added. A fantastic panoramic window gives views wherever you turn, creating an environment to enjoy a childhood dream for many – your own personal, WORKING crane. The crane still spins when controlled from the cabin, but amazingly they've fitted a luxury double shower and designer loo into the crane which still work when the crane is spinning!!!

Entry to the crane itself requires no exertion although it is a little cramped in the central column lifts to the main bedroom area. The top picnic area and crane cabin are accessed via a ladder from the main bedroom, but you rarely feel enclosed or adverse to heights.

A fantastic breakfast is included, delivered magically via the internal lift to your bedroom.

LOCATION AND ACTIVITIES

Close to the city centre of Harlingen you're only 10 minutes walk from the shops and restaurants of this thriving Dutch seaside town. Harlingen itself is only an hour by car from Amsterdam, or by train direct to the dockside (Dokkade) station, this is a must-try property, with an equally fascinating Lifeboat and Lighthouse hotel 5 minutes walk away. With a crane at your disposal, you're sure to find yourself spinning the platform instead of watching the supplied DVD's.

"A bedroom in your own personal, working crane"

Dockside Crane Hotel
Dokkade 5
Harlingen
The Netherlands
www.GoUnusual.com/CraneHotel

- Breakfast provided
- Restaurants nearby

"Adventure without risk is

Disneyland."

Doug Coupland

HET KLEINE PARADIJS
ROMANTIC TREEHOUSES

Created with ecologically treated wood, well insulated and maintained, the two treehouses at 'Het Kleine Paradijs,' provide a peaceful and romantic base from which to explore the region. After you've climbed the staircase and seen the stained glass of your front door, you'll appreciate the effort made for even the smallest detail. Supplied with electricity they boast heating, cooking facilities, a sofa and double bed.

Showers / WC are located in a separate building on the ground floor.

LOCATION AND ACTIVITIES

Het kleine Paradijs is close to Friesian cities like Sneek and Bolsward and only a 25km drive from regional capital Leeuwarden. ''Noflik,'' the oldest bistro/bar in Friesland, only a short walk away, provides a cozy atmosphere, great food and warm welcome.

Catch sunshine and nature together on the spacious bridge-terrace, looking out over the idyllic Friesian view with a cup of tea or coffee.

Should you wish to take a break from relaxing, there are plenty of outdoor activities such as canoeing, walking or cycling. Even ice skating in winter!

"Friendly treehouses"

Het kleine Paradijs
Meilahuzen 9
8734 GA Easterein
Netherlands
www.GoUnusual.com/Hetkleineparadijs

183

Supertrips, úw startpunt voor de meest bijzondere hotels en bed and breakfast locaties voor een romantisch weekendje weg of een bijzondere vakantie. Van een overnachting in een safaritent, tipi of iglo tot slapen in een boomhut, ijshotel of uitkijktoren.

www.supertrips.nl

"You don't choose the day you enter the world and you don't chose the day you leave. It's what you do in between that makes all the difference."

Anita Septimus

"NOT I – NOT ANYONE else,

can travel that road for you,

You must travel it for yourself."

Walt Whitman

HAYEMA HEERD
SLEEP IN STRAW

LOCATION AND ACTIVITIES

Hayema Heerd is situated just 15 minutes drive from the centre of Groningen, where you'll find restaurants, shops, bars and historical sights. It is about 25km from the Wadden Sea, a UNESCO World Heritage site. In the morning guests are offered a generous breakfast buffet with several bio and local products.

A range of unique activities can be arranged including 'be a farmer in two hours', a trip on the elliptigo exercise bike, a sailing safari or hike to the Wadden Sea.

"Farm fantasy on straw beds"

Hans & Wil Hoogeboom offer different options for straw-themed accommodation on their Hayema Heerd farm. Maybe a classic hayloft straw bed? Or a straw castle with drapes, fancy chandeliers and soft cow skins on the floor? Perhaps a straw igloo with clear glass central viewing panel for guests to stargaze from the comfort of their bed?

With a thick layer of fresh straw covered by a comfortable mattress, sleeping on straw is soft, springy, comfortable and warm all year round.

Hayema Heerd
Jensemaweg 3
9883 TH Oldehove
Netherlands
www.GoUnusual.com/HayemaHeerd

CONTROVERSY TRAM HOTEL
CITY TRAMS AND RAILCAR CARRIAGE ROOMS

In addition, the train carriage - a restored railcar, sleeps four and has a fantastic Mexican themed interior with a giant jacuzzi in the shape of a huge sombrero. As well as a double bed in a boat, the interior has a really funky theme. The two doubles are really comfortable and the bathroom is spacious.

LOCATION AND ACTIVITIES

About an hour from Amsterdam, Controversy is only 10 minutes from the dunes and beaches.

"Fantastic for families"

Frank and Irma Appel have restored a 4-berth train carriage and four wonderfully themed tram bedrooms in either end of two city centre tram railcars, that used to run on the streets of Amsterdam and Germany. With double bed, shower and toilet facilities, these represent a fantastic Bed and Breakfast location.

Next to the carriage is the Appel house, Controversy - named after their love of the similarly titled Prince album. You can't help but join in the lifestyle that Frank and Irma have created! They themselves sleep inside a London Double Decker bus, installed in the living room, and their kitchen and breakfast area is a converted French van. Their house is decorated with cars, and motor paraphernalia.

Controversy Tram Hotel
Koningspade 36, 1718 MP
Hoogwoud
The Netherlands
www.GoUnusual.com/ControversyTramHotel

• Bed & Breakfast
• Recommended for children

"Once you have travelled, the voyage never ends… The mind can never break off from the journey."

Pat Conroy

SILOGIE
GRAIN SILO CONVERTED TO LUXURY SUITES

LOCATION AND ACTIVITIES

The mill is on the outskirts of the village of Epe with moorland, woods and the wide plains of the river IJssel around it. Walkers, cyclists and nature lovers will enjoy the area as the woods practically start at the door. The towns Zwolle, Deventer and Apeldoorn are only a short distance away for gourmet delights restaurants and shopping.

The former hall has been turned into a studio with space for 10 large easels. A number of courses in art are available and an exhibition space for contemporary art has now been established in the gallery offering changing exhibitions.

"Back to nature art and wildlife in complete comfort"

Respecting the original architecture, the mill was renovated to create a large painting studio, gallery, and lovely guest rooms including a luxury suite in the grain silo tower with its own private entrance. This suite has a large four-poster bed and a bath with panoramic countryside views. The designer seating area has a flat-screen TV with a DVD player and rooms include a pantry with coffee maker, kettle and refrigerator.

Silogie
Paasvuurweg 7A
8161CA Epe
Netherlands
www.GoUnusual.com/Silogie

CAPSULE HOTEL
ESCAPE OVERNIGHT IN YOUR OWN SURVIVAL POD

Based at the Verbeke Foundation, your room is a bright orange survival pod which once saw service on an oil rig platform. Originally built in 1972 they are 4.25 metres in diameter and unaltered apart from the addition of a lock on the outside and an 'emergency' chemical toilet inside. While not everyone's luxury choice, each pod provides cosy protection from the elements for up to three occupants.

First created for accommodation as an art project in 2004, owner Denis Oudendijk has 8 different models ready for use and is currently working on additional locations in central Amsterdam and Nantes, France.

The bathroom facilities are non-existent / basic, with baby wipe towels and bottled water to replace traditional shower and washroom facilities. Thankfully the pods are located on land - which makes them much more comfortable and there are bathroom facilities in the main building 50 metres from your pod.

LOCATION AND ACTIVITIES

As with CasAnus, (see entry) the Verbeke Foundation is an art incubator and there are some fascinating Art ideas in development. If you're keen to venture further afield, the Verbeke Foundation is 30 minutes drive from the historic town of Bruges. It is equally close to the sandy coast.

"Cheap, quirky escape pod in an art foundation"

Capsule Hotel
Verbeke Foundation
Kemzeke,
Stekene 9190
Belgium
www.GoUnusual.com/CapsuleHotel

• Breakfast provided
• Restaurants nearby

AIRPLANE SUITE
LUXURY SUITE IN CONVERTED PLANE

Once the transport for top bosses of the German Democratic Republic government, this 1960 Ilyushin 18 has been converted to a single luxury suite for 2. The plane is 40 metres long and now comes equipped with a little more luxury than it's former owners would have approved of - let alone publicly enjoyed!

With a Jacuzzi, shower, infrared sauna, mini bar, flat screen TV's (three of them!), Blu-ray DVD / entertainment combo (plus a selection of DVD's), and a pantry with coffee/tea making facilities, you can enjoy a great deal of comfort - while still sleeping on a plane.

A welcome package is provided on arrival, with a snack, coffee or tea. They also provide bathrobes and slippers to borrow. Planes can be a bit stuffy inside, and the unobtrusive air conditioning assures you of a level of overnight comfort. In addition to offering luxury accommodation, the airplane can also be hired as a meeting space for ten to fifteen people. While most will arrive by car, you could always arrive in style to the airport direct.

The cockpit is left untouched, so although flights are limited to your dreams, there is plenty of airplane fun to be had as you pretend to be pilot and chief steward - or stewardess!

This plane flew dignitaries including Erich Honecker during it's early life as a political transport for the favoured government leadership. Converted to commercial airline use in 1964, it flew up to 120 passengers and 4 crew in slightly less comfort with East-German airline, Interflug until 1986. Destinations included Cuba, China and Vietnam as well as Soviet bloc Russia.

LOCATION AND ACTIVITIES

Teuge airport is at the centre of the city triangle of Deventer, Apeldoorn and Zutphen. These historic cities offer a varied shopping experience with some nice boutique shops. At the airport itself, you can book an aerial experience tour, by plane or helicopter, and for those with an interest flight, try a flying lesson if you want to learn to ride the skies. For serious thrill seekers, why not consider a parachute jump or a ride with a stunt plane!

"Fly to your dreams in this converted plane"

Vliegtuigsuite
De Zanden 61B
Teuge (near Apeldoorn)
7395 PA
The Netherlands
www.GoUnusual.com/AirplaneSuite

• Breakfast provided

EUROMAST TV TOWER
2 LUXURY ROOMS ON TOP OF A TV TOWER

The Euromast tower is a feature of the skyline of Rotterdam, and has been a regular tourist attraction since it was built in the 60's. Already known as a great lunch and dinner venue, there are also 2 suites - Heaven and Stars, perched 100m above the city for advance booking.

After the crowds have gone, suite occupiers are left to the night skyline in luxury with polished wooden floors, comfortable double beds, minibar and room service through to 1am.

The view across the town and to the docks below is endlessly fascinating, so some might not use the free wireless internet provided. The larger of the 2 suites, Heaven, has a great view of the docks and can provide a child's cot. It also has a great shower and something that we hadn't seen before – designer black loo-roll. The smaller suite, Stars, looks over the Rotterdam city, and has a bathroom Jacuzzi.

Balcony access is from 10pm through to 10am, so you have plenty of time to enjoy view.

Now fitted with central heating the suites are warm all year round. The only worry perhaps, is that not only are you able to look out – the occupants of the other suite can look in from the shared balcony… so consider shutting the curtains if your pyjama's aren't suitable for external viewing!!

LOCATION AND ACTIVITIES

Euromast has a restaurant/brasserie but you're only a short taxi ride from the centre of Rotterdam, with restaurants bars and nightlife, so aren't short on things to do. Take one of the yellow water taxis for a tour to see the docks, or just to try a different way of getting about.

Euromast is in the Parkhaven, but consider the parking restrictions if you arrive by private car, or perhaps take a taxi. While parking carnets are available from the tower shop, it can prove expensive if you leave your car for the day, and you'll need to perhaps feed the meter again when you'd rather be tucked up in bed or enjoying breakfast.

"Birds-eye viewing from your bedroom"

Euromast,
Parkhaven 20
3016 GM
Rotterdam
The Netherlands
www.GoUnusual.com/Euromast

• Bed & Breakfast
• Brasserie/Restaurant

"Too often travel, instead of broadening the mind, merely lengthens the conversation."

Elizabeth Drew

ZEELANDMOLEN
RESTORED DUTCH WINDMILL

LOCATION AND ACTIVITIES

The old port town of Brouwershaven is situated on 'Schouwen-Duiveland', the most northern Island of Zeeland in the South-West of the Netherlands, one hour drive from Rotterdam, Antwerp and around two hours from Amsterdam. It is connected with other islands and the mainland by three bridges and a dam.

The windmill is situated next to the marina and has a great view over Grevelingen lake.

There are several of the best Dutch beaches nearby where you'll find opportunities for kite surfing, sand sailing and surfing. You might also wish to visit the pretty towns of Zierikzee or Burg-Haamstede.

"A classic windmill in Holland"

ZeelandMolen
Noordwal 3
4318 BR Brouwershaven
Netherlands
www.GoUnusual.com/ZeelandMolen

Built in 1724, the windmill was renovated in 1969 and turned into a house to live in. Interestingly, the original cog mechanisms in the mill were preserved on the third floor and the mill can still turn its blades, although it can no longer grind grain. Surrounded by a garden that looks out over the town and marina, inside you'll find a modern designer kitchen, cooking range, oven, microwave and dishwasher - indeed all the comforts of a modern house inside a traditional building. There is even free WiFi!

CASANUS
GIANT INTESTINE SCULPTURE THAT YOU CAN SLEEP IN

This is one of those indescribable properties that leaves people stunned when you say that you slept in a giant model of a human intestine. From the initial Why? to the usual How and Where, and of course eventually, What was it like??

It's an Art Sculpture - created by Joep Van Lieshout and there's a normal double bed inside. There is an electric point, heater, as well as a shower and toilet at the other end of the room, with hot water.

Breakfast is provided in the nearby main building.

LOCATION AND ACTIVITIES

In search of an extraordinary original location? The Verbeke Foundation will suit you down to the ground!

Founded by art collectors Geert and Carla Verbeke-Lens, The Verbeke Foundation is a private art site which first opened doors to the general public on June 1st of 2007. As a 'refuge of arts' the domain offers chances to young / less renowned artists and holds an impressive collection of modern and contemporary art. Geert and Carla started collecting art in the early 1990's. Their interest was initially drawn by abstract painting. Later the focus of the collection shifted to collages and assemblages of mainly Belgian artists. In recent years the collection was further expanded to current art and bio art – art with living organisms.

Culture, nature and ecology go hand in hand in the Verbeke Foundation.

"Our exhibition space does not aim to be an oasis. Our presentation is unfinished, in motion, unpolished, contradictory, untidy, complex, inharmonious, living and un-monumental, like the world outside of the museum walls. You will find no flamboyant sensational buildings here, but rather, a refreshing, unpretentious place to look at art and a subtle criticism of the art world" - Geert Verbeke

Verbeke Foundation
Kemzeke,
Stekene 9190
Belgium
www.GoUnusual.com/CasAnus

The South of Belgium: Where Style and lifestyle are so close!

Ever wondered why ageless stars like Audrey Hepburn and Diane von Furstenberg are effortless style icons? They were born in Brussels, capital of French-speaking Belgium, of course!

With the likes of creators like Olivier Theysken (a favourite of Nicole Kidman), Jean-Paul Knott (a former Yves Saint Laurent designer), Olivier Strelli (who made suits for Mick Jagger) or Laeticia Crahay (head of accessories at Chanel), Brussels & Wallonia are a hotbed for the latest and most stylish trendsetters in the world, often acclaimed by magazines such as VOGUE or ELLE.

For a girly weekend, or a must-do break for the well-informed traveller, why go anywhere else than Brussels & Wallonia?

www.belgiumtheplaceto.be

"I haven't been everywhere, but
it's on my list."

Susan Sontag

THE ATOMIUM
PRIMARY SCHOOL GROUP SLEEPING SPACE INSIDE

The Atomium is an icon of Brussels built for 1958 World Fair Exposition, at a time when the belief in progress, science and modernity was immensely strong. The structure symbolises an iron crystal, magnified 165 billion times.

Spanish artist Alicia Framis was commissioned in 2005 to create an educational project based on the building's characteristics and features as well as its history and its symbolic value. The kids sphere captures the optimism of a future enabled by technology and science, in a way that reflects the insights of the world in the 21st century.

One ball of The Atomium has been divided in separate functions: mini spheres (water molecules) suspended from the ceiling to sleep in, the floor for workshops/playground, a 'petit club sandwich' and washing facilities. Children spend a night at The Atomium marveling at the panoramic view of Brussels from its spheres; and make the most of their visit by discovering other symbolic parts of Brussels from a unique vantage point.

LOCATION AND ACTIVITIES

Fifteen H2O (raindrop) mini spheres hang from the ceiling, three meters above the floor. These are translucent with lights inside. During the day, they are suspended high in the ceiling. The floor is then available for childrens' workshops. At night the mini spheres 'fall' from the sky, like raindrops. When they reach the floor they are used as little shelters to sleep in and the floor space transforms into a small city of mini sphere raindrops. The floor is made of soft recycled material.

DETAILS FOR GROUPS

Children and their accompanying adults arrive at The Atomium at 6pm. Generally a film is put on, and all meals and facilities are laid on in the Sphere. The children sleep in small groups (3-4 maximum) in the mini-spheres. The next morning, after breakfast in the panoramic restaurant, there is a presentation about The Atomium. The experience ends at 10am in the morning.

The capacity is for between 10 (min) and 24 (max) children, plus up to 2 accompanying adults on Monday, Tuesday and Thursday - outside of official Belgian holidays. Unfortunately, access to the kids sphere is necessarily via stairs.

"Kids room in Iconic Landmark"

The Atomium
Atomium Square
1020 Brusselles
Belgium
www.GoUnusual.com/TheAtomium

- School Groups Only
- Dinner, Bed & Breakfast

HOTEL WELCOME
AROUND THE WORLD IN 17 ROOMS

Ideally situated on the former Fish market, a 10-minute walk from the Grand Place, this hotel is exceptional, unusual and surprising. It offers a veritable round-the-world journey in its 17 guest bedrooms, each of which is decorated differently to evoke a different country. The owners, Sophie and Michel Smeesters, are seasoned travellers and have brought back from their travels much of the furniture and ornaments in the hotel. The result is a universe that unfolds as you go from one room to another. The en-suite bathrooms are also decorated in the styles of the different countries, and the Deluxe rooms and suites have a spa bath or a double jacuzzi with a shower.

Michel had already built a fantastic reputation with the restaurant when the couple decided to renovate and extend the property in 2001. The attention to detail and service that made the restaurant a success are still evident to hotel guests and you can see the passion for excellence throughout the property.

Standard themed rooms include Congo, Kenya, Vietnam and Japan - where not only the furnishings, but also maps on the walls, tribal masks and door surrounds evoke a flavour of each country.

Larger deluxe rooms include Bali, with its intricate wood carvings, Tahiti with bamboo and tropical birds and India, where statues of Ganesha and Shiva look down on you.

Suites offer not only a sitting room, but also a balcony - or in the case of their newest Belgian suite, two rooms providing for family groups of up to 5 guests.

LOCATION AND ACTIVITIES

You will find yourself in the heart of Brussels, in a beautiful hotel where top-quality service matches the attention to detail of the decor. Every room offers a different world travel experience in this cosmopolitan city filled with history.

"A world journey in the centre of Brussels"

Hotel Welcome
23, Quai au Bois-à-Brûler
1000 Brussels
Belgium
www.GoUnusual.com/HotelWelcome

- Breakfast provided
- Restaurants nearby

HOTEL BLOOM!
ROOMS DECORATED WITH MURALS BY YOUNG ARTISTS

In 2008, the owners of Hotel Bloom wanted a way to renew the hotel and invited creative artists from different countries across Europe to paint murals on the wall of bedrooms, offering something unique and interesting for guests. Now guests can choose their own favourite room with a hand painted fresco on the wall, often based on the artists own interpretation of the word 'bloom'.

The bloom idea comes from the hotels location near the botanical gardens, where flowers, plants, trees and herbs blossom year-round. The hotel echoes the true meaning of the word "To bloom" as it really has brought a creative vibrancy and a unique, funky style. In order to keep blooming, Hotel BLOOM! organises an Art'n BLOOM! event a few times a year. This exhibition gives young artists and designers the opportunity to show their work and is worth making a special trip to see.

At BLOOM! you'll find no stuck up rules. Forget dress codes, room service or bell boys. They attract people that have an open mind - from the sudoku offered at the breakfast table to the freshness of the rooms, they do things differently!

Like the smell? Or the background music? Both the fragrances used in guest toiletries and the music you'll hear in the lobby have been specially commissioned – and are available to purchase.

Feel relaxed, laid back and totally be yourself as they offer an easygoing stay. Bloom! stands out from the ordinary because they think and do things out of the box. UHOTW urge you to visit and see why.

TO DO

You are within 15 minutes of the main Brussels shopping area (Grandes Magasins) on foot, and near all the main historical sights (grande Place etc.) within a 20 minute walk. Alternatively take the tram or metro, with the station 'Botanique' just 20m from the hotel door. The main rail station of Gare du Nord is 500m away. Trams really are a fantastic way to get around. Easy, cheap and stress free, although of course a taxi is the choice if you're pressed for time. The tram museum underwent a large restoration recently and is a very worthwhile trip. (www.trammuseum-brussels.be).

"287 artists from different European countries"

Hotel Bloom!
Rue Royale 250
Brussels
Belgium
www.GoUnusual.com/HotelBloom

• Breakfast provided
• Bar / Restaurant on-site

BE MANOS

FUNKY PHOTOS OF OWNERS FRIENDS ON EVERY DOOR

A 1920's building, very close to the Thalys & Eurostar terminal, transformed to a metropolitan design hotel, by Constantin Poulgouras - the recognised creator of the first designer hotel in Brussels. Using ideas from a collective of European designers, this is a masterclass of how to turn old town houses into magnificent palaces.

Creative and Funky, the reception is like an intimate nightclub. Ascend the lift to the rooms and on every floor you'll see photo montages on the walls of friends and colleagues of the owner, immortalised by photographer Carol Kohen on room doors in etched aluminium and on stunning photo canvases. As you walk through the hotel you'll find their discrete presence in a variety of playful hotel scenarios, including a pillow fight, will bring a smile to the most jaded traveler.

It's a nice touch to discover that these are real people, rather than just hired models from an agency. These images add to the funky-yet-informal feel of the property. A bonus is that if the furnishings and fixtures are something you like, they're available to purchase, with details provided in the room or at the front desk.

TO DO

You are a 10 minute walk from the exit of the Eurostar, and within a tram ride of the whole of Brussels. European connections via Thalys are at your feet, so this property lends itself as a base for exploration not only of Brussels, with it's fascinating streets, curios, food and monuments – but Paris, London and Amsterdam too.

As a capital of culture, Brussels needs little introduction, and everywhere worth visiting is within reach of the trusty tram, or for time pressed travelers, a taxi.

"...close to Eurostar and Thalys terminals"

beManos Hotel
23 Square de L'aviation
Brussels
B-1070
Belgium
www.GoUnusual.com/BeManosHotel

• Breakfast provided
• Bar / Restaurant on-site

PANTONE™ HOTEL
ROOMS THEMED BY THE PANTONE COLOR CHART

The Pantone Hotel™ invites you to experience the city of Brussels through a lens of color and a spectrum of comforts. Colours used are referenced to the globally recognized Pantone Color Matching System® - that allows standardized colour reproduction. By standardizing the colours, different manufacturers in different locations can all refer to the Pantone system to make sure colours match without direct contact with one another.

Impeccably designed by Michel Penneman and Oliver Hannaert, the hotel showcases the color of emotion with a distinctive hue on each guest floor. Rooms feature unique photography by esteemed Belgian photographer Victor Levy. From a design perspective, the hotel is built on an exceptional use of contrast; a white canvas provides clean space for saturated colors to pop. Both bright primary colours and warmer tones, displayed in photos, furnishings – even the chairs and coffee cups, add mood shifting sparkle.

From the moment you arrive, this "hotel of colors" will awaken your senses to an array of delights and playful surprises. Vivid or subdued, for business or leisure, this unique boutique hotel perfectly suits a savvy palette and colorful imagination.

Guests enjoy great beds, LCD TVs, and central air conditioning with individual controls. Many rooms in the upper floors benefit from a rooftop view of Brussels.

LOCATION AND ACTIVITIES

The Pantone Hotel™ is located at the heart of a trendy shopping district - Avenue Louise and Toison d'Or. Whether you are looking for clothes, shoes, books, tableware, jewellery, cosmetics, ... you can find near anything locally.

"Welcome to the center of the color universe!"

The Pantone Hotel™
Place Loix 1
Brussels
B-1060
Belgium
www.GoUnusual.com/PantoneHotel

• Breakfast provided
• Bar / Restaurant on site

GÎTE "LA CLASSE"
CONVERTED SCHOOL

Anne and Jean-Luc Laloux specialise in architectural photography, and travel the world in search of exceptional homes designed by the best contemporary architects. This enriching experience has inspired them to create beautifully appointed holiday accommodation which combines both the conviviality of group living with the aesthetic pleasure of great design.

La Classe, (The Classroom), is exceptional and a long way from any school memories that you may have! The quality of the materials, the wonderful use of space, the selection of designer furniture, the highest standard of facilities and fittings – all the ingredients to create a special atmosphere are here: the rest is up to you.

Architects, landscape designers, environmental sociologists, all agree that we think 'differently' in different places. There can be no doubt that your stay here will make you look at life in a new way.

Fancy a drink in the huge living room with its 9m long bar? A Hitchcock thriller in the projection cinema with hi-fi surround sound system, perhaps? Or how about a fun evening spent playing table football and listening to the old Wurlitzer juke box?

Relaxing in the luxurious furniture, you can indulge yourself in the sort of conversation we never seem to have time for any more; meanwhile the kids can play on the basketball court, or with the giant board games in the playroom.

LOCATION AND ACTIVITIES

Situated in the village of Denee, which is part of the commune of Anhee, La Classe used to house both the municipal offices and the village school. It is situated in the heart of the village, less than 100m from the village square, on a one-way street at the far end of the square.

Denee is in the heart of one of the most beautiful regions of Belgium, only 5 minutes away from the Molignee valley and the Abbey of Maredsous, the gardens of Annevoie, close to Dinant and Namur.

"Trendy and filled with history"

Gite La Classe
1, Tienne Piot
Denee, Namur
Wallonie
Belgium
www.GoUnusual.com/Lactases

• Self catering
• Suitable for Groups 10+
• Minimum stay requirement

GÎTE "LES DUVES"
RESTORED SAWMILL WITH RIVERSIDE LOCATION

Stunning open-plan self catering accommodation for 2-4 people in an old sawmill, converted and furnished with a contemporary feel. Interior design and furniture created by the owners, Anne and Jean-Luc Laloux, a couple of globe-trotting photographers who have worked with many international interior design magazines.

The mill, built of local stone, has an exceptional riverside location next to te river Burnot, providing an idyllic summer escape.

The property has a private terrace and garden benefiting from the gentle sound of water flowing past for an amazing ambiance. Next to the main building are a couple of covered outbuildings used for petanque and table tennis.

The living area is on the ground floor with 3 modular divan beds on wheels, built to the owners' own design. Not only are they comfortable, they are functional room dividers. Entertainment includes TV satellite, Hi-fi, DVD, Wi-Fi. As well as central heating there is also an open fireplace.

Kitchen facilities, (gas hob, electric oven with hood, fridge-freezer, dishwasher, Nespresso machine with capsules), are all high quality designer fittings.

The adjoining bedroom has a twin bed and connects to the bathroom (bath and shower), and separate toilet.

This is the second of Anne and Jean-Luc Laloux entries to the UHOTW guide (see La Classe).

LOCATION AND ACTIVITIES

Situated in the heart of one of the most beautiful regions of Belgium, the accommodation is close to Namur and Dinant, Maredret, St Gerard, Floreffe – The gardens of Annevoie – Bambois Lake – Golf at Profondeville – Canoeing on the River Lesse – The chateau of Freyr – Mozet, Crupet etc (some of the villages classified as 'the most beautiful villages in Wallonia')

"Self catering with a designer touch"

Les Duves
36, Rue de Arbre
Bioul, Namur
Wallonie
Belgium
www.GoUnusual.com/LesDuves

• Self catering
• Suitable for Families
• Minimum stay requirement

MANOIR DE LÉBIOLES
VERSAILLES OF THE ARDENNES

Located in a magnificent countryside setting, at the heart of the Ardennes forests, "Le Manoir de Lébioles" welcomes its guests to a superb setting of discreet luxury, privacy and top-quality service.

One of the most beautiful buildings of the city of Spa, it was constructed for Georges Neyt (1842-1910), an extraordinary visionary, diplomat and foreign envoy who was alleged to have been the illegitimate son of King Leopold I. He had the house built for his own use between 1905 and 1910, but unfortunately did not live long enough to enjoy his "Little Versailles of the Ardennes" for long.

A family home of some glamour until 1980, it was sold and had success as a Hotel de Charme until 1999 whereafter it was mis-managed and fell into disrepair. New owners were installed and an international team of architects ensured that on reopening in 2006, the new building has every modern comfort, convenience and purity of line, without losing its ancient, graceful, soul.

The 16 suites at "Le Manoir de Lébioles" offer all you could wish for. Each one has its own style and charm. The large suites will help you forget your daily routine: relax in the bath in the turret, read a book in the alcove, or simply stretch out in front of an open fire: these are just some of the possible ways to rest and relax.

A pool and wellness centre adjoins the main hotel whose gourmet restaurant, features the 16 point Gault Millau dining of Olivier Tucki.

LOCATION AND ACTIVITIES

From the manicured grounds you'll enjoy fine sunset views of the Ardennes that match superlative creations in the kitchen and understated luxury in the suites.

This property once again lays claim to its former glory and regains the justified title of jewel of the Ardennes Forest.

"Plus Valet Quam Lucet -
More to it than meets the eye"

Manoir de Lébioles
Domaine de Lébioles 1/5
4900 Spa
Belgium
www.GoUnusual.com/ManoirdeLebioles

• Bar / Excellent restaurant on site
Check for opening

LA BALADE DES GNOMES
THEMED SUITES AND TROJAN HORSE

Ten of the most extraordinary bedrooms hidden in an unassuming farmhouse up a pleasant - but not particularly noteworthy - country lane, designed and built by architect and visionary hotelier Mr Noël. Originally opening an innovative restaurant, La Gargouille (the Gargoyle), specialising in delicious dishes using local ingredients and bio-organic produce, he has taken inspiration from fairytales to construct these amazing bedrooms, next door to the restaurant.

Defying normal classification, these rooms highlight incredible imagination, attention to detail and sheer audacity to delight guests.

Claiming inspiration from Robert Louis Stevenson and Lewis Carroll does insufficient justice to this fairytale property.

- Sleep with a mermaid in your own sailing yacht, floating in a pool, with a starry sky above... reached via a sea captains snug with oak panels - on the third floor of the farmhouse !...

- A wheeled Trojan Horse, with access by a lowering drawbridge to enter a beautifully hand crafted, wooden interior !...

- Or a wine cellar, with vines, barrels and oak wine press furniture !

- Maybe a trolls habitat, complete with goldfish swimming in the stream running through your bedroom? ...and many more besides...

Rooms are stunning!! A really imaginative and other-worldly place.

LOCATION AND ACTIVITIES
15 minutes' drive from Durbuy. [10 km - 6.5 miles]

"Sailboat in a pool on the 3rd floor ..and more"

La Balade des Gnomes
20, Rue Remouleur
6940 Heyd (Durbuy)
Belgium
www.GoUnusual.com/LaBaladedesGnomes

• Bed & Breakfast
• Restaurant next door
(check opening)

QUARTIER LATIN
CONVERTED CHURCH

The Quartier Latin is an 18th century Jesuit church, restored and converted into a delightful, centrally located, hotel complex. It was considered sufficiently charming, that the company that completed the conversion created a specific hotel division to manage the church, rather than sell it on.

It's a lovely place to stay, relax and be pampered – as well as a great place to eat or drink. The restaurant / brasserie offers a wide choice of meals and suggestions ranging from the fast lunch to the gourmet menu.

It all began with an architectural competition where applicants were requested to submit a proposal for the renovation and re-use of this site, which had received "historic monument" status from the Royal Monuments and Sites Commission.

Although the winning bidder, HOUYOUX was initially only in charge of building and promoting the facility, the project proved so attractive that eventually HOUYOUX decided to manage it. This unusual diversification process by the company led to the creation of its third subsidiary on 25 June 1992: S.A. Quartier Latin.

Now extended with the addition of a spa, Quartier Latin has rooms in both the old church and new extension – so ask if the more impressive church rooms are available.

LOCATION

Less than an hour from Central Brussels and located in the town centre of Marche-en-Famenne, next to the pedestrian precinct, Quartier Latin's rooms and suites combine the richness of the past and the contemporary comfort of a four-star hotel.

"Links terrific Belgian food & drink with historic surroundings and spa facilities"

Quartier-Latin
Rue des Brasseurs 2
6900 Marche-en-Famenne
Belgium
www.GoUnusual.com/QuartierLatin

• Breakfast provided
• Bar / Restaurant on site

223

EURO SPACE CENTER
ASTRONAUT TRAINING IN EUROPE!

The Euro Space Center is a recreational & educational discovery center about space, related science and technologies. Unique in Europe, it allows families to live as real astronauts and to experiment astronaut training for a number of residential programmes targeting French, Dutch, English and German speaking groups.

Space camps are suitable for youngsters from the age of 8 within the scope of a school project or on holidays. Programs include various workshops, simulation exercises, observations and lectures on space and its exploration.

The main goal here is to enable young participants to experience the training that has been set up for the astronauts during the 50 years of space exploration. Every year The ESC hosts groups from all around the world to stay and visit. About 100,000 youngsters between 10 and 16 years old have already taken part in the programs, coming from Belgium, Europe and elsewhere. They gain their own experience in simulators, training machines, workshops, on courses of 2 to 6 days in duration.

FACILITIES AND LOCATION

As well as a full size mock-up of the Space Shuttle and ESA's Columbus - an element of the International Space Station, a number of micro gravity simulations, and exercises are available. Both an indoor and outdoor programme of activities is available and includes for families:

The complex includes a restaurant, activities & accommodation with space themed rooms where participants sleep in spacious 6-8-bed rooms with shower and washbasins. Bathrooms are in the hall or en-suite.

Situated in the Belgian Ardennes, about 90 minutes from Brussels, or an hour from Liege, the centre is alongside highway E 411 – exit 24.

"Space - The Final Frontier, in Luxemburg"

Euro Space Center
Rue devant les Hêtres 1
Transinne 6890
Province Of Luxemburg
Belgium
www.GoUnusual.com/EuroSpaceCenter

- Suitable for Groups (min 12)
- Family weekends & Individuals
- Full board packages provided

225

Central Europe
Germany, Poland, Czech Republic, Austria, Latvia

Key

Entries in **Bold** typeface indicate full page entries with a photo.
Others are additional indexed entries.

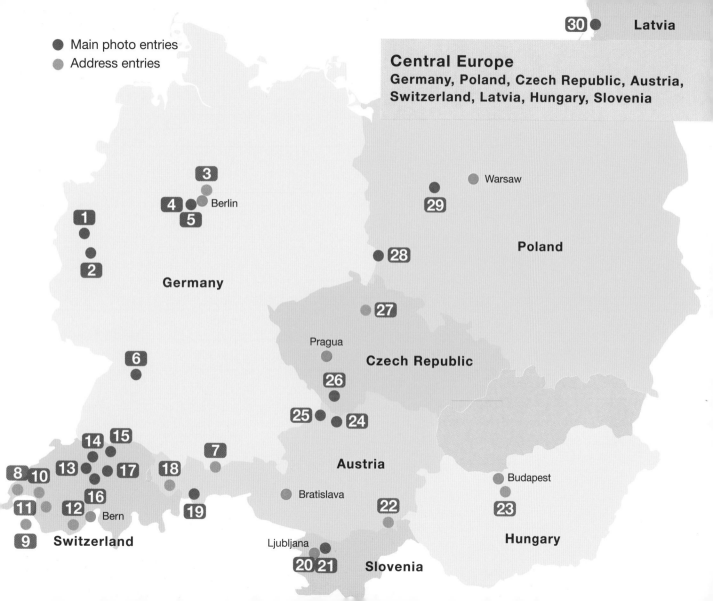

Central Europe
Germany, Poland, Czech Republic, Austria,
Switzerland, Latvia, Hungary, Slovenia

Latvia

Warsaw

Poland

Germany

Berlin

Czech Republic

Pragua

Austria

Bratislava

Budapest

Hungary

Ljubljana

Slovenia

Bern

Switzerland

● Main photo entries
● Address entries

DASPARKHOTEL - BERNE PARK
SLEEP IN A CONCRETE PIPE

The idea of Andreas Strauss and first created in Linz, then Ottensheim, Austria, these concrete tubes provide basic hospitality on a pay-what-you-wish donation basis, thanks to support from Emschergenossenschaft and Gafög.

Constructed from 9,5 tonne concrete drain pipe sections they are cool in summer and warm at the end of season. They're simple - but functional, and a great bet if you're cycling or want a change from camping.

The rooms are round like a barrel and provide you with maximum comfort in a minimum of space. You sleep on a double wide Eurofoam mattress supported by an ergonomic slatted frame by Optimo. Surprisingly comfortable, the pipe offers a full head height interior with a light. In the storage box right next to the bed you will find fresh pillows, blankets and sheets - plenty for even the coolest summer nights. Your luggage can be tidily stashed away in the storage space beneath and next to the bed.

DasParkHotel don't want your digital camera or mobile phone to die mid-trip and additionally provide a 220V outlet for charging your electronic devices.

Bring your own toiletries (toothbrush, soap, towels...) as all other facilities (loo, shower, food etc.) are provided locally.

LOCATION AND ACTIVITIES

Upon booking you will receive a code to allow entry to your personal suite. For the period of your stay dasparkhotel remains your all hours access safety zone - the charger for your personal energy reserves.

Because DasParkHotel uses sanitation, breakfast and other hotel facilities from existing public infrastructure, it is possible for them to work with the very simple, user-friendly "pay as you wish" donation pricing.

A night costs just as much as you can afford or want to pay.

"Robust, simple and safe"

DasParkHotel
Berne Park
Bottrop-Ebel
Near Essen
Germany
www.GoUnusual.com/DasParkHotel-BernePark

- Web booking only
- Basic facilities
- Donation for payment

HOTEL IM WASSERTURM
LUXURY HOTEL IN WATERTOWER

As Cologne grew into the industrial powerhouse that it is today, the requirement for an underground water main to feed the growing city's needs meant that this 35m high, 19th Century watertower, was no longer required. Standing derelict for many years, it took the genius of French interior designer Andrée Putman and the courage of a team of investors to turn what used to be Europe's largest water tower, into the amazing 5 star hotel that we enjoy today.

This one-of-a-kind experience remains one of the most architecturally stunning hotels in Germany. Classified as a heritage site, you will find an extraordinary interior design of timeless modernity behind its 140 year-old walls. The imposing 11m high entrance hall with its catwalks, 2-Star Michelin 'La Vision' restaurant on the top floor - mezzanine Presidential suite, grand conference facilities - all share the status that this massive building imposes.

LOCATION AND ACTIVITIES

With a city-centre location, Hotel im Wasserturm is near all the main sights, either on foot, by public transport or taxi.

Cologne Cathedral is the most visited attraction and well-known heritage building in Germany. With its two 157 m spires it has been the city's landmark for hundreds of years.

The Schokoladenmuseum (Chocolate Museum), shows the 3000 year-old history of chocolate and its production.

Equally perhaps, you might like to experience a panoramic view of the historic city centre around the cathedral on board a comfortable tourist boat.

"Luxurious Landmark building"

Hotel im Wasserturm
Kaygasse 2
D-50676 Köln
Germany
www.GoUnusual.com/HotelimWassertum

- Breakfast available
- Excellent restaurant

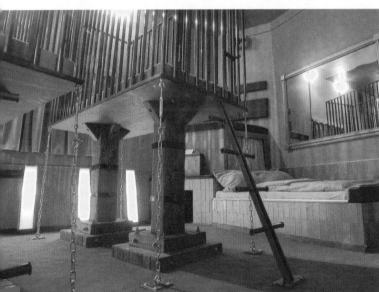

PROPELLER ISLAND CITY LODGE
FLYING BEDS AND UPSIDE DOWN ROOMS

This is an extraordinary location. All rooms and objects were created by the German artist Lars Stroschen. Much more appropriate than "hotel" is the designation "living in a work of art". 30 rooms with an absolutely unique and personal ambience. "Unique" is meant literally, for the entirety of all furnishings and other objects you will discover here are custom-made, individual handiwork. None can be found anywhere else on this planet - one could consider the CITY LODGE to be a museum with guest accommodations or a stay-in work of sculpture. The rooms are designed and constructed without compromise varying from the tame to the extreme, and provide the opportunity to more or less alter your perspective of reality - according to your taste and sense of adventure.

Room examples - these are some of the most outrageous of the 30 on offer, but there is great variety from fun through funky, to fetish.

Upside Down: The furnishings hang from the ceiling and you sleep and sit in comfortable boxes beneath the floorboards. Surreal!

Mirror: This diamond-shaped room is completely laid out with mirrors to give you the impression of living in a kaleidoscope.

Prison Cell: A friendly prison cell with a hole in the wall leading to freedom on the balcony with a parasol.

LOCATION AND ACTIVITIES

The hotel is just outside the centre of Berlin, but within walking distance of shops, restaurants (including an excellent South American restaurant) and bars. Transport by u-bahn, bus and taxi is cheap and easy.

The nearest U-Bahn stop is Adenauer Platz.

"Justifies a trip to Berlin on it's own!"

Propeller Island City Lodge
Albrecht Achilles Str. 58
Berlin
Germany
www.GoUnusual.com/PropellerIslandCityLodge

- Breakfast provided
- Restaurants nearby

HUETTENPALAST

CARAVANS AND WOODEN HUTS INSIDE FORMER FACTORY

LOCATION AND ACTIVITIES

This creative playground, where guests spend the night in an old caravan or a wooden hut gives you the feeling of a touch of summer – even in winter!

Sit and swing in front of the huts or walk in flip-flops from your caravan, toothbrush in hand to the showers without getting cold - or wet!

"Outdoor Living - Inside! "

Hüttenpalast is a treasure trove of retro-theme happiness. With your fun accommodation actually inside this former vacuum-cleaner factory, guests can choose the back to nature pleasure of cozy caravans, designer bedrooms or wild wooden cabins. Even better, this accommodation is in Central Berlin, with the amenities of a modern building, including guaranteed warmth spring, summer, autumn and winter.

Huettenpalast
Hobrechtstraße
Berlin, Neukölln 12047
Germany
www.GoUnusual.com/Huettenpalast

• Café for breakfast on site

V8 HOTEL
CAR THEMED HOTEL

Part of the Meilenwerk classic car restoration complex on the old Zeppelin airfield near Böblingen, ten of the 34 car themed rooms have had extreme makeovers to allow you to sleep in a Mercedes, Morris Minor, Cadillac or Volkswagen.

There are ten styled theme rooms, singles, doubles, plus a family room and the spacious Zeppelin suite, with a fantastic panoramic view. The 24 standard rooms have some great wall photography but the theme rooms really take the automotive element to a new level.

Perhaps you wish for the luxury of sleeping in a converted white Mercedes bed – bright and polished from the carwash? Maybe airbrushed custom paintwork and chrome is more your style in the Tuning bedroom? Or the 53 Beetle Herbie parked up as a bed in the Petrol Station room?

A Cadillac bed and artwork themed around the drive-in cinemas of the 50's and 60's, or a room themed for the outdoors, in V8 Camp?

While everyone will have a favourite, the Morris Minor car bed in the 'Workshop' room – complete with mechanic under the car, deserves special mention. Your bed is hoisted on lifting jacks, and your bedside table a drum of oil. A mechanics workbench your writing desk.

The top Zeppelin suite occupies the once control tower of the airfield and the V8 hotel itself occupies the original Bauhaus-style (1928) airport hotel building, now completely restored and updated as a listed building in its own right.

LOCATION AND ACTIVITIES

The hotel is a 5 minute walk from Böblingen S-Bahn rail station on line S1, which connects to the S2 and S3 lines if you're visiting one of the many trade shows in Sindlefingen or arriving at Stuttgart airport.

"Petrol Head Heaven - with Dreams to match !"

V8 Hotel
Graf-Zeppelin-Platz, Wolfgang-Brumme-Allee
Böblingen, Baden-Württemberg
Germany
www.GoUnusual.com/V8Hotel

"A tourist is a fellow who drives thousands of miles so he can be photographed standing in front of his car."

Emile Ganest

HOTEL PILATUS-KULM
TOP OF THE MOUNTAIN VIEWS

After all the clean mountain air you'll be ready to enjoy delicious dining in the Queen Victoria dining room, so named after the Royal visit of the First Queen Victoria. Starry skies are a wonder to enjoy, returning to the warmth of a warm fire in the bar.

LOCATION AND ACTIVITIES

In summer, take the Golden Round Trip, to include a stay in Hotel Pilatus-Kulm, travelling up the mountain by cable car, and descending by Cog Railway. Then enjoy the boat trip from Alpnachstad - a 5 minute walk from the Cog railway station, back to Lucerne.

"Stunning views.
Amazing location."

This mountain top hotel can be reached by cable car (all year opening) or the world's steepest cogwheel railway (May-November). Recently restored to the historic grandeur of its opening in 1890, rooms have spectacular views. Rooms are fantastically comfortable and with the freshness of the mountain air you'll sleep incredibly well, waking up refreshed by the first of the sun rays.

Hotel Pilatus-Kulm
Schlossweg 1
Kriens, Lucerne 6010
Switzerland
www.GoUnusual.com/HotelPilatus-Kulm

JAILHOTEL

PRISON, CONVERTED TO HOTEL AND NIGHTCLUB

The Jailhotel is located in the heart of Lucerne, right in centre of the Old Town, and only a few minutes away from the lake. This former prison was built in 1862 and was converted into a prison hotel in 1999, the first in Switzerland. It's a great budget choice for visitors and offers a number of conference rooms and business facilities.

A total of 56 different rooms and suites are offered from original "Unplugged" rooms where you have a bunk bed and more authentic prison experience, to the larger "Most wanted" rooms, and largest Theme suites of Prison Governor, Library, Barabas and Falling Water.

The thick walls, solid doors and barred windows retain their original feel and as you're sleeping in a converted cell, shouldn't expect your room to be huge. Private bathrooms are small-but-adequate with a shower. The Unplugged rooms have their private shower across the corridor.

LOCATION AND ACTIVITIES

Close to the rail station, there is a public parking garage called "Altstadt" only 5 minutes walk away from the hotel for guests arriving by car.

Although you've got a city centre location, the street is quiet and you're close to the main sights of the city. Just off nearby Lowenplatz in a small park, we recommend viewing the carving of the dying lion by Bertel Thorvaldsen. Visitors also flock to the Verkehrshaus der Schweiz (Swiss Transport Museum), about 10 minutes away using public transport, and we recommend a full day to visit its exhibits.

"Great location and budget prices"

Jailhotel
Löwengraben 18
Luzern
Switzerland
www.GoUnusual.com/Jailhotel

• Breakfast provided
• Bar / Restaurants nearby

THE PROPOSAL

BECOME RESIDENTS IN ART - AS PART OF AN ART INSTALLATION

In the beginning of November, 2011 the artists gallery, THE PROPOSAL, opened its doors to the public in a quiet city centre courtyard in Zurich. THE PROPOSAL offers the unique experience of spending a night in it's own Bed & Breakfast. Guests can experience being part of an art gallery during an exhibition and while exhibitions are being installed. They become "residents in art". Visitors are not just ordinary guests of the gallery. THE PROPOSAL is organized as an association so visitors can become members of this remarkable art club.

The gallery does not just present art; THE PROPOSAL philosophy is to showcase prototypes of possible artwork, encouraging debate about the necessity and originality of art.

Art as Experience - an experiential exchange between the viewer and the exhibition. The guest lives, sleeps and eats in and with the art.

Memories - opportunity through accommodation to immerse into the artwork and to reflect about the exhibition themes. This creates unforgettable experiences and memories.

A Dynamic Space - art installations that change from month to month means guests will return in order to experience the new look of the space.

Part of the Process - a focus on making a visit to the gallery to a truly experiential process. Visitors not only view the Proposals but can also participate in their realization.

There are 2 bedrooms, both with Queen beds. One is located inside the art installation, and the second is inside a converted 1977 Peugeot J7 van sprayed Chrome and Silver, which some would consider a classic work in itself!

LOCATION AND ACTIVITIES

You are just 5 minutes away from the Zurich-Wiedikon train station and shops; tram and bus stops are just a few steps away. The Zurich main train station is reachable in 5 minutes by the S-Bahn (urban-rail) train or in 10 minutes by tram 14.

"Live, Sleep and Dream Art"

THE PROPOSAL
Dubsstrasse 33a
Zurich
Switzerland
www.GoUnusual.com/THEPROPOSAL

• Bed & Breakfast
• Cafe/Restaurant nearby

IGLU-DORF
IGLOO RESORTS IN MULTIPLE LOCATIONS

Adrian Günter built his first igloo in 1996, to better enjoy the mountain and first powder snow of the day. Following an avalanche of interest from friends wanting to sample an igloo night, he increased the number of igloos and opened the "small world in white" in 2006, with 6 villages across Andorra, Switzerland and Germany now accepting guests.

Moving three thousand tons of snow every December to build each village, Adrian invites artists from all over the world to craft sculptures inside each village. With only an ice pick, motor saw and shovel, artists produce seals, arctic wolves, polar bears and whales as well as swirling designs and patterns illuminated by candle light to look over the guests from the walls.

The villages are open from Christmas day through to the beginning of April each year, snow conditions permitting.

With 10,000 visitors in 2010, all ages have enjoyed the cosy hospitality of an expedition sleeping bag and sheepskin rug, from the youngest 6 month and 2 day old baby to an 83 year old lady guest.

Available in locations in Andorra, the Swiss Alps and at the Zugspitze, villages accommodate up to 52 guests in different igloo options from romantic igloos for 2, to larger family and standard igloos for up to 6 people. Prices are lowest midweek, rising at weekends and during the New Year. They include food, some non alcoholic beverages and the use of sauna or whirlpool facilities.

The team has even built a church including an altar for a wedding party. Every village is equipped with a large igloo lobby and bar where the evening meal is served.

LOCATION AND ACTIVITIES

The Engelberg resort is very easy to reach as it is only 2 1/2 hours from the airport to the top of cable car by train from Zurich.

While the snowboarding and snowshoe activities available at all the villages are to be expected, your overnight package includes the use of a communal sauna or whirlpool. After spending the day on the piste in the fresh mountain air, there are few things more relaxing than sitting in a whirlpool viewing a sunset over the mountains.

"An Igloo world in white !!!"

Iglu-Dorf Engelberg
Engelberg-Titlis
Engelberg
Switzerland, Andorra, Germany
www.GoUnusual.com/Iglu-DorfEngelberg

- Dinner, Bed & Breakfast
- Group bookings welcome

HUSKY-LODGE

SLEEP NEXT TO THE HUSKY KENNELS

Guests sleep in wooden cabins next to the working dog kennels at Husky-Lodge. You can join them in their training runs all year round as they pull sledges and bikes around the natural woodland, fields and mountain trails.

If you're a Siberian Husky lover, you get to appreciate at first hand how loveable - and hard working - these dogs are, whatever the weather, returning to relax in your cabin by the wood fire.

LOCATION AND ACTIVITIES

The Husky-Lodge is located at the entrance of Bisisthal, approximately 2 km east of the village center of Muotathal, located in the center of Switzerland. You'll find a mountain valley, village and a town with down to earth culture and unparalleled scenery.

As well as Siberian huskies, there are possibilities for other outdoor activities like ice climbing, snowshoeing, hiking, climbing, team events etc. At nearby Hölloch, you'll discover one of the longest caves complexes in the world - well worth a booked visit.

"These hard working dogs love to run!"

Erlebniswelt Husky-Lodge
Postfach 34
Muotathal, Schwyz 6436
Switzerland
www.GoUnusual.com/Husky-Lodge

247

SCHNEEDORF IGLOO VILLAGE

IGLOO HOTEL, IN THE MIDDLE OF A SKIING RESORT

Spend the night in Austria's first Igloo village, amidst a fantastic mountain panorama in one of the 18 Classic or Romantic two and four-persons-igloos. The Schneedorf offers you a mix of unforgettable impressions and activities to enjoy the starry winter sky after the lifts have shut.

From the usual winter sport activities like skiing, snowshoe hiking, snowboarding or toboggan, at the Schneedorf you can also have a relaxing, luxurious time in their mountain sauna - made out of local Zirbenwood. At night, nestle down in a fantastic warm expedition sleeping bag, cuddling on the sheepskin, or having champagne with your partner in one of the individual created and carved Romantic igloos.

"For many guests the overnight stay in a hotel made totally out of snow is an entirely new and intense experience. In such an environment it is almost impossible for our visitors not to forget the stress of everyday life. Quite often it means for them, that childhood dream comes true", says Dr. Alexander Klaussner. "By the way, we celebrated more than a dozen successful wedding proposals last winter."

Together with the sculpture-decorated main igloo with space for more than 60 people, the snowbar and a separated lounge area, the Schneedorf is perfectly suited for exclusive events and parties.

LOCATION AND ACTIVITIES

Situated in the skiing resort of Hochoetz/ Ochsengarten, more than 2020 meters above sea level, close to Sölden in the Ötztal-Valley.

"An igloo bed overnight"

Schneedorf Igloo Village
A 6433 Ötz, Hochötz
Ötz
Tirol/Ötztal
Austria
www.GoUnusual.com/Schneedorf

• Dinner, Bed & Breakfast
• Group bookings possible

249

HOSTEL CELICA

FORMER PRISON TRANSFORMED INTO ARTISTIC HOSTEL

Hostel Celica is much more than a hostel. Following the departure of the Yugoslav army in 1991, this former prison has been transformed into a hostel, art gallery, tourist attraction and meeting place with cultural events, winning many accolades. It hosts fantastic music nights.

Due to the slow bureaucracy of the former Yugoslavia, transferring ownership, of these former army barracks, from government ministries to the peoples' collective set up to run the hostel by the city of Ljubljana, was a surprisingly lengthy undertaking. However, the patience and tenacity of the artists who have supported this project has finally been repaid. This well admired conversion to a 'funky, hip' hostel, is the recipient of many accolades for the cell rooms and overall hospitality.

Lonely Planet proclaimed Hostel Celica as the world's Hippest hostel #1. Rough Guides included it into the world's ultimate 25 places to stay.

There are 20 cell rooms on the first floor, each decorated by a different artist. Some have added mezzanine bunk beds to use the small room space efficiently and most have retained the prison window bars for an authentic confinement feel. None of the cells are en-suite, however the toilets upstairs are clean and functional, if not a little busy in the mornings.

LOCATION AND ACTIVITIES

Hostel Celica is in the heart of Ljubljana, just 300m from the central railway and bus station and approximately 700m from the city center, (Prešeren Square and old town).

If you're arriving by air to Brnik Airport, there is a bus service to Ljubljana main bus station, around 5 minutes walk away from the hostel. Alternatively try their airport shuttle connecting the hotel and airport direct which is good value when booked in advance.

"Jailhouse Rock!"

Hostel Celica
Metelkova 8,
Ljubljana SI 1000,
Slovenia
www.GoUnusual.com/HostelCelica

HOSTEL TRESOR
BANK CONVERTED TO HOSTEL

Dormitory rooms have been rearranged into several smaller "vaults" to offer guests a degree of intimacy, with bunk beds arranged in cages that once held valuables and deposit boxes. Two lively common areas are the heart of Tresor. The high atrium area with a sky ceiling is at its most vibrant during daylight hours while the former bank vault in the basement comes into its own in the evening.

LOCATION AND ACTIVITIES

The Tresor Hostel is situated right in the heart of Ljubljana town centre, close to Prešeren Square, Three Bridges, Dragon Bridge or Ljubljana Castle. Near the hostel you can explore a number of boutique stores, enjoy fresh fruit and vegetables at the market, have a drink in coffee shops and bars that line the banks of the Ljubljanica river, visit theatres, museums, galleries or explore the night life in Ljubljana.

"Every room a different foreign currency"

By transforming a grey and dull former bank into a lively, creative hostel, Hostel Tresor has made the only currency that matters the happiness of guests. Keys aren't needed to access rooms at the Tresor, as they're opened by card, pendant or bracelet.

Hostel Tresor
Čopova 38
Ljubljana 1000
Slovenia
www.GoUnusual.com/HostelTresor

"Man cannot discover new oceans

unless he has the courage to lose sight

of the shore."

Andre Gide

PIXEL HOTEL
UNCONVENTIONAL ROOMS SPREAD ACROSS CITY

A project for the Linz 2009 European Capital of Culture created a hotel where creatively designed rooms are dispersed across the city. Pixel im Hof provides a 1960's camping caravan, installed inside an industrial warehouse. Pixel mit Garten is a flat and shopfront converted to showcase an indoor garden with attached bedroom. Pixel in der Textilpassage provides a living space on four separate levels, dominated by a floating island where you'll find your bed for the night. It also includes the Neverland den, conceived with a ceiling too low for adults and filled instead with kids toys and pillows. Pixel in der Volksküche includes a remote controlled fold away bed in the building that is home to Architekturforum Oberösterreich – itself a showcase of modernist, minimal decoration. Pixel am Wasser provides a room on 1958 tug, MSZ Traisen, now restored and lying at anchor in Linz harbour.

All over Linz, these unconventional but unused premises have been converted into hotel-style rooms. They're in a mixture of residential areas, downtown, industrial zones and working-class neighbourhoods – and guests will find different experiences in each.

The features and conveniences of a modern hotel room are maintained: double bed, living area, bathroom, minibar, WiFi, TV and maid service. For breakfast, guests are provided with vouchers to nearby cafés. Local restaurants serve as the hotel's dining room and neighbourhood pubs with their character and local colour more than make up for the absence of a traditionally overpriced hotel bar.

LOCATION AND ACTIVITIES

Rooms all have a king size bed, bathroom with shower, WC, TV, and WiFi. Some also include the use of 2 bicycles to explore the city.

"Individually designed rooms"

Pixel Hotel
Altstadt 28
4020 Linz
Austria
www.GoUnusual.com/pixelhotel

• Bed only provided
• Breakfast offered in nearby cafe

DASPARKHOTEL - OTTENSHEIM
CONCRETE SEWAGE PIPES

Designed from the outset to use world standard concrete drain or sewage pipe sections, a second venue is now open near Essen in Germany. It has even been copied in Mexico.

The idea of Andreas Strauss in 2004, the first rooms in Linz were created thanks to the support of Emschergenossenschaft and Gafög. Now in nearby Rodlgelände, Ottensheim, rooms are accessed by a digital keypad, whose code is provided by the self service website upon booking acceptance.

The beauty of these pipes is that their concrete utilitarian look needs little alteration to make them habitable - a coat of varnish is all that is necessary. The tubes have also have received wall paintings by the Austrian artist Thomas Latzel Ochoa to make them seem a little more user friendly.

Each tube weighs 9,5 tonnes – so they are incredibly robust and need little maintenance. Advanced locks are fitted so they're secure too. Like cave hotels, DasParkHotel are cool in the summer, and perhaps still warm in winter, although at the moment the hotel is only open from May to October.

Once inside, facilities are basic - a double bed, light, power point, blanket and light cotton sleeping bag are provided. The toilet and (cold) showers are a couple of minutes walk away, with details provided on booking.

Rooms are payable on a donation only. There is no set pricing and we recommend you check the hotel website link for online availability.

LOCATION AND ACTIVITIES

Located in a lovely spot next to the Danube in Ottensheim municipal camping area the tubes have had a several seasons of use but are still clean and functional.

While there are many restaurants in the town square 15 minutes walk away, we particularly recommend the El Danubio campsite bar and it's host Sergio, who will prepare excellent rib and fried potato dinners a minutes walk from your room. Details of places for breakfast, drinks and bathroom facilities are provided in the joining instructions.

The campsite has beach volleyball courts, a kiddie paddling pool and nearby spots for swimming in the Danube. The site is next to the 2008 Rowing World Cup regatta course.

In Ottensheim itself, you can book river trips on the Danube, however most people choose to take the train or bus to visit nearby historic Linz.

"Concrete pipe is warm in winter, cool in summer"

DasParkHotel
Rodlgelände
Ottensheim
Austria
www.GoUnusual.com/DasParkHotel

- Bed only provided
- Web booking only

KRUMLOV TOWER

BEDROOMS WITHIN A CASTLE TOWER

Krumlov Tower is located on the right bank of Vltava river of historic Cesky Krumlov, one of the most popular holiday destinations of the Czech Republic after Prague, hosting a number of cultural festivals and events each year.

The tower itself was built at the end of the 15th century as a round bastion - part of the town fortifications – with original wall fragments and a conical ridge-tiled roof. In 1805 Prince Josef II zu Schwarzenberg, (ancestor of the Minister of Foreign Affairs of the Czech Republic), agreed for the building to be converted to a guardhouse, by providing a chimney and accommodation facilities. Now it's been updated with more modern features to provide accommodation for guests.

LOCATION AND ACTIVITIES

Comprising two apartments over three storeys, sleeping a maximum of six in each apartment, across a combination of double and twin beds.

Cesky Krumlov is built around a 13th-century castle with Gothic, Renaissance and Baroque elements, surrounded by a maze of twisting alleys and crooked cobblestone streets. Recognized as a UNESCO World Heritage Centre, it is an outstanding example of a medieval town, whose architectural heritage has remained intact thanks to a peaceful evolution over more than five centuries.

The main attraction of the city is the Gothic castle from 13th century, the second largest castle complex in Czech Republic. Cesky Krumlov is also considered the cultural centre of the Czech Republic, and you will find here many museums and art galleries in the town.

For the more adventurous, hire a bike and ride around the Cesky Krumlov or consider the free flowing Vltava river, popular with rafting enthusiasts, where excursions on canoe and kayak can be arranged.

As with many vibrant cities in Eastern Europe, there are bars, restaurants and clubs, some of them with live music. Inquire when you book for details of the best places to go.

"Bedrooms built into the Old Town walls"

Krumlov Tower
Pivovarska, 28
Cesky Krumlov 381 01
Czech Republic
www.GoUnusual.com/Krumlovtower

- Bed and Breakfast
- Restaurants nearby

BAUMHAUS HOTEL
TREEHOUSES

Choose one of five cosy tree houses situated 8m to 10m up a tree in the Gruengeringelten recreational park outside Görlitz. First open in June 2005, it is arguable whether it is the first tree house hotel in Germany or the craziest. Whatever the decision, these two storey dwellings are furnished in a crazed rustic style, with brightly coloured walls and off-angle windows and are sure to entertain.

Odd shaped beds are the norm here as you won't find any straight walls.

Each tree house contains an 'emergency toilet', but if only for the sake of the cleaners, a central toilet block is provided on one of the lower decks with running water. The central area also contains a particularly German addition – a mini bar filled with beer ready for evening guest celebrations. Tree houses additionally share an extraordinary open air, chilled water shower with a metal grid floor, so you can see the ground below you. Whether this is for health reasons, for waking up, or perhaps because of the provision of the guest mini bar, sobering up is unknown.

Bedrooms are 'rustic' and perfectly functional for an amusing night. It's fun and quirky!

Some tree houses have small balconies and each tree house is themed according to the regional tradition and myths of trolls and fairy folk. Get in tune with your inner troll to enjoy this resort!

Electric heating is provided for those brave enough to extend the summer open season into November and risk snow. A breakfast buffet is served in the main site restaurant.

LOCATION AND ACTIVITIES

Görlitz is in the easternmost part of the Federal Republic of Germany. By car, leave the A4 (Dresden-Bautzen-Görlitz) autobahn at Görlitz, towards Rothenburg. Around a mile (2km) from Zentendorf pick up signs to the site.

The adventure park hosts events and concerts throughout the season.

"First treehouse hotel to open in Germany"

Baumhaus Hotel
Zentendorfer Str. 55
Neißeaue 02829
Germany
www.GoUnusual.com/BaumhausHotel

• Bed & Breakfast
• Recommended for children of all ages

BLOW UP HALL 5050
MONOCHROME HOTEL AND ART INSTALLATION

LOCATION AND ACTIVITIES

Halfway between Berlin and Warsaw, the hotel is less than 10 minutes walk from the Old Market Square, which is a lively area offering a wide selection of bars, restaurants and cafés next to the 16th Century city hall. The hotel is 10 minutes from the central train station and around 20 minutes by car from low-cost airline served Poznań Lawica airport.

"A world of white, black and chrome"

No central reception area. No room key. A black-faced lift, taking you to a black corridor with black doors. No room numbers. Clicking a button on the iPhone offered for use during your stay lights a screen next to your room – and the door opens.

Taking styling queues from cult 1966 movie Blow Up, the old brewery complex has been transformed into a combination of the Art hotel with stylish shopping arcade, dance centre and the contemporary gallery Art Station 5050.

Blow Up Hall 5050
Bul.Kościuszki 42
61-891 Poznań,
Poland
www.GoUnusual.com/BlowUpHall5050Hotel

"If at some point you don't ask yourself, 'What have I gotten myself into?' then you're not doing it right."

Roland Gau

KAROSTAS CIETUMS
MILITARY PRISON

LOCATION AND ACTIVITIES

Ever since the first years of its existence, Karostas Cietums on the Baltic Coast has been a place to break people's lives and suppress their free will. Facilities are basic and you can sign up for experiences where you'll discover some of the harsh treatments experienced by prisoners.

Beds are hard and blankets thin.

To ensure that every participant is aware of, and willing to comply with, the treatment they'll received - they are required to sign a special agreement in advance.

"Do you think you're tough enough to do time?"

This military prison has remained unchanged since its beginnings in Tsarist times. Thankfully no longer in use for official guests, visitors may now experience the harsh prison life in a variety of ways, from a short overnight tour, to themed activities for groups.

The prison hosts a variety of events based on recorded history and experiences, but it's not an ordinary museum and certainly not a luxurious overnight property.

The prison is open from 1st May till 30th Sept or by prior arrangement.

Karostas Cietums
Invalīdu Street 4,
Liepāja, Karosta
Latvia
www.GoUnusual.com/KarostasCietums

265

Europe

France

Key

Entries in **Bold** typeface indicate full page entries with a photo.
Others are additional indexed entries.

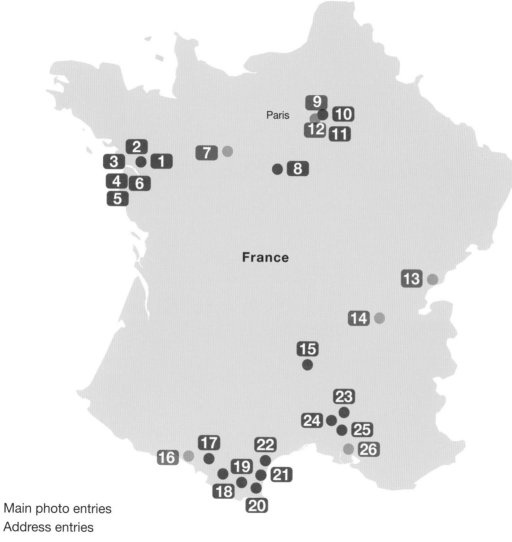

Europe
France

Paris

France

● Main photo entries
● Address entries

"The journey is the reward"

Steve Jobs

LE VOYAGE EXTRAORDINAIRE
SLEEP IN A PACKING CASE

LOCATION AND ACTIVITIES

Facing the Loire river and Ile de Machines - the Jules Verne themed activity park, Le Voyage is close to the sights, restaurants and nightlife of Nantes City centre.

One of the "must visit" attractions will be the Ile de Machines, which as well as the workshops and design studios, offers tours atop a giant mechanical elephant able to convey up to 50 people around the park. There is also the recently opened (2012) three storey high fairground carousel, detailed with amazing fantasy creatures, amusing for adults and children alike.

"Inspiration to simply pack up
your belongings and travel"

Based on the writings of Nantes-born science fiction pioneer Jules Verne, Le Voyage Extraordinaire is quirkily themed to suggest souvenirs from the travels of his literary characters. The main bedroom is inside a giant packing case, reached by a catwalk. A mezzanine childrens bed, accessed by ladder, is perched on top of the bathroom featuring a 'magic mirror' designed to intrigue and delight younger fans. There is also a modern kitchen with self catering facilities suitable for a family of 2 adults and a couple of smaller children plus a crate/lounge area where you'll discover an electronic library of the collected works of the author.

Le Voyage Extraordinaire
Quai de la Fosse,86
44000 Nantes
France
www.GoUnusual.com/LeVoyageExtraordinaire

HOTEL POMMERAYE
ARTIST DESIGNED HOTEL ROOMS IN CENTRE OF NANTES

Each year, Hotel Pommeraye invites a local artist to develop a project at the hotel itself. This artist is then given free reign to dream up one or several works, drawing inspiration from the hotel. Launched in 2005, the artists inject creativity to a hotel located right in the centre of town.

This six-storey building dates back to the end of the 18th century and has a total of 50 rooms. Over time, modern facilities, (such as a lift), have been fitted.

- 2006 Delphine Brétesché brought the basement to life and blasted it into the lobby during half a dozen off-the-wall performances.

- 2007 Micha Deridder decided to decorate the rooms specifically for lovers and loners.

- 2008 video director Charlie Mars, shot his first short film, 'Nightmare Hotel' here in 2008.

- 2009 Amélie Labourdette, inspired by road movies, conjured up images of cult film scenes in a surprising set of vibrant pieces, coupled with dreamlike photography.

- 2010, the hotel was delighted to host Michel Fourquet and his sharp-witted work with tooth-picks.

- 2011, it was under the name of "Hotel of the two sweaters" that Frederico Pelligrini has created art to view.

In addition, for 6 years, room 108 of Hotel Pommeraye has been turned into a radio studio once a month for the programme 'dans les draps les mots' (words between the sheets). Broadcast live on the Nantes station, it features interviews with poets invited to take part in lectures hosted by the Nantes Poetry House.

LOCATION AND ACTIVITIES

Hotel Pommeraye is located in Nantes city centre, in the heart of the Graslin district and its pedestrian streets, just a few metres away from historic Passage Pommeraye.

A parking space for your vehicle is provided around the corner from the hotel. Night parking is free.

"City centre hotel with artist creativity in rooms"

Hotel Pommeraye
Rue Boileau
Nantes 44000
Pays de la Loire
France
www.GoUnusual.com/HotelPommeraye

VILLA CHEMINÉE
ROOM ATOP AN INDUSTRIAL TOWER

This artistic project was designed by Japanese artist Tatzu Nishi for the Estuaire 2009 Nantes-Saint-Nazaire art event.

A juxtaposition of classic 1970's French gîte rental property sitting atop a 15m high stack, styled on the chimneys of the Château de Fer power station - the largest coal fired plant in France, alongside.

Sleeping 2, there are excellent views across the Loire from the upstairs bedroom.

Downstairs there is a small kitchen, table, a couple of chairs, shower and bathroom facilities. Outside the gîte there is a small garden atop the tower with all round views across the Loire. The property is open all year round and a wood fired heater is provided for the winter months.

LOCATION AND ACTIVITIES

Situated near Cordemais, on the banks of the Loire, it is about 35km from the centre of Nantes.

"Visually stunning to look at, and to look from"

Villa Cheminée
44360 Cordemais
France
www.GoUnusual.com/Villacheminee

CHÂTEAU DU PÉ
ARTIST THEMED SUITES IN COUNTRY HOUSE

LOCATION AND ACTIVITIES

Château du Pé is located in Saint-Jean-de-Boiseau, overlooking the Loire. It is on the Loire cycle path and part of the Nantes Métropole urban community.

By car: It is a 20 minute drive from Nantes to the Château du Pé. Drive on the D723 from Nantes, then turn off towards Saint-Jean-de-Boiseau following directions for Centre Ville and then church/town hall. The entrance of the park of the Château is 150 m away from the church.

Saint-Jean-de-Boiseau is also located half-way between the two bacs de Loire (ferry boats) Indre-La Montagne and Couëron-Le Pellerin.

"6 bedroom choices with artistic merit"

The local community of Saint-Jean-de-Boiseau acquired the 18th Century Château du Pé in 1997 and, with it's seven hectares of grounds, decided to renovate it as a cultural centre with hostal facilities. The Estuaire Nantes-Saint Nazaire art event team took charge to chose a number of artist 'couples' to create six unique and individually designed bedrooms. From a reproduction theme in "La Grande Question" to the minimalist "Antichambre", where all furniture is hidden in the walls and floor, behind every one of the 6 doors, you'll find a room that provokes comment.

Château du Pé
44640 Saint Jean de Boiseau
Nantes
France
www.GoUnusual.com/ChateauDuPe

"The world is a book and those who do

not travel read only one page."

St. Augustine

DE LA TERRE À LA LUNE
THEMED FOR PLANNING A TRIP TO THE MOON

With a spaceship kitchen area, exposed brick walls and chesterfield sofa this apartment provides a quirky showcase for a variety of Verne paraphernalia.

LOCATION AND ACTIVITIES

If two bedrooms are not enough for your needs, this room can connect to Le Voyage Extraordinaire (see separate entry) next door to create an amazing family celebration venue. The apartment is equally suitable for couples or families, however there is so much to see, you'll have to pry the young and young-at-heart away!

"You will leave inspired"

Furnished like a movie set, De la Terre à la Lune - From the Earth to the Moon, is based on Jules Verne's 1865 novel. There are two adult bedrooms - one minimalist luxury with claw footed bathtub, the other in the centre of a paper-strewn workshop. Kids will love the 'crows nest' bed reached by a steep ladder and perched on top of the pod-styled bathroom. Doors are heavy steel constructions and there is a life-sized street lamp in the lounge and 1800's model glider suspended from the salon ceiling.

De la Terre à la Lune
Quai de la Fosse, 86
44000 Nantes
France
www.GoUnusual.com/DeLaTerreALaLune

"There are no foreign lands. It is only
the traveler who is foreign."

Robert Louis Stevenson

CABANE DE CAPITAINE NÉMO
THEMED APARTMENT OF JULES VERNE CHARACTER

From the moment you type in a secret code and collect your key, you know you are going to have fun in Captain Nemo's cabin. Made to resemble where the book hero might have lived when on shore, the tiny apartment is filled with Jules Verne books, quirky artwork and fascinating steampunk-style gadgets. A shower with complicated dials and valves? A sink with beer tap pipework? Of course! Perhaps too, a small breakfast bar/kitchen with an antique toaster as a light fixture? Captain Nemo's living room with a sofa bed is upstairs, accessed by a steel staircase, and across a catwalk you'll find the futon-style double bed in a low-headroom nook.

For those who observe closely there is a secret escape route from the bedroom down a ladder to the bathroom!

LOCATION AND ACTIVITIES

Located in the centre of Old Nantes, 5 minutes walk from the Château des Ducs de Bretagne. You're also near the other Yann Falquerho properties of Le Voyage Extraordinaire and De la Terre à la Lune and of course the magnificent Ile des Machines Jules Verne inspired workshops

"Artistic and Fun!"

Cabane de Capitaine Némo
12 Rue de Briord
44000 Nantes
France
www.GoUnusual.com/LaCabaneDeCapitaineNemo

LES ALICOURTS RESORT TREEHOUSES
FAMILY TREEHOUSES IN LOIRE HOLIDAY RESORT

The Alicourts Resort covers an area of nearly 60 hectares in the heart of the Loire Valley with picturesque views and top rate facilities. On 30 acres of preserved forest the resort has constructed 8 beautifully crafted treehouses to provide a truly unforgettable experience.

Suitable for families as well as couples, there are different types of treehouses: for 2, for 4 and up to 6 people at a height between 3,50 meters to 7,50 meters off the ground.

All tree houses have ecological toilets and garden furniture. Although there is no running water in the treehouses, nor electricity, toilets and showers are available close to their accommodation.

In the treehouses, you're provided with candle lights and torches. Washing facilities are in the main buildings and a morning breakfast is provided, delivered to the bottom of your tree!

LOCATION AND ACTIVITIES

The campsite offers quality services and installations, spacious camping pitches and fully equipped Loire Valley cabin rentals. Providing camping, caravanning, chalet and treehouse holiday options, you couldn't do better.

The resort has a restaurant, a take-away, a supermarket and a bar.

Throughout the season, there's a wide range of sporting and leisure facilities and activities and special events organised for both adults and children.

Choose either the swimming/fishing lake with its sandy shore or the Aquatic park with its wave machine and slides. The on-site Spa/Balneo centre with Jacuzzi provides a heaven of peace and relaxation, offering a wide range of spa treatments carried out by trained beauty therapists.

A very large range of activities can additionally be arranged: 9 hole golf course, waterski cableway, mini-golf, tennis, football, gym, skatepark, canoes, etc... as well as the chateaux and gardens of the Loire Valley itself.

"Treehouses for romance or families with children"

Les Alicourts Resort Treehouses
Domaine des Alicourts
Pierrefitte sur Sauldre 41300
France
www.GoUnusual.com/LesAlicourtsResortTreehouses

• Vacation Rental
• Recommended for children

HOTEL PARTICULIER MONTMARTRE
DESIGNER PROPERTY

Hôtel Particulier Montmartre is an impressive white town house, surrounded by a delightful garden, landscaped by Louis Benech (who redesigned the Tuileries gardens). Formerly owned by the Hermès family, it is hidden in a secret hillside passageway to offer seclusion and serenity in an arty district of Paris.

Small, but beautifully quirky, it offers guests an intimate atmosphere combining Art-house opulence, creativity and refined creature comforts. The five spacious suites offer garden views and have been individually designed with input from Morgane Rousseau incorporating artworks from different contemporary artists.

Each of the hotel's five rooms offers great furnishing and many surprises, none more so than the loft penthouse suite "Curtain of Hair". Accessed by a private spiral staircase, it is open-plan and, with it's skylight window, offers a panoramic view of Paris. The charcoal and cream decor has been kept plain and in the salon space of this suite, a Napoleon III style bathtub reigns supreme while dollhouse furniture peeks out from various nooks as if the scales of size have been tampered with. Black and gold striped carpeting blends with the cashmere drapes and upholstery.

Those less observant, may feel that they are being watched as indeed there are painted Barbie doll eyes hidden in different parts of the Suite, spying upon the traveller. It is a little eerie and surreal – yet all the same interesting and amusing. Looming large is a huge photo portrait of 2 young women by the artist Natacha Lesueur, hiding their eyes behind strands of hair, hence the name "Curtain of Hair".

The other suites offer equal interest, and even the smallest Junior Suite "Vitrine" provides a fascinating collection of provocative curiosities, perhaps more suited to a medical school, displayed in a 19th century cabinet.

TO DO

The hotel is set in a private cobbled passageway (Witch's Rock Passage) between avenue Junot and rue Lepic on the hillside of Montmartre in the 18th arrondissement of Paris. A 5 minute walk from the Sacré Cœur, discover this historic area and visit the Musée de Montmartre, previously home to Renoir, or meander through the Place du Tertre.

From here you can discover the Montmartre vineyard, the bohemian rue Lepic and rue des Abbesses or take the metro to the flea markets of St Ouen.

"UHOTW top tip... request a candelabra lit breakfast in your room - or on one of the garden terraces in summer."

Hôtel Particulier Montmartre
Pavillon D
23 avenue Junot
Montmartre
Paris 75018
France
www.GoUnusual.com/HotelParticulierMontmartre

- Breakfast provided
- Restaurants nearby

MAMA SHELTER
ECLECTIC, FUN AND FUNKY AMBIANCE

In the historic Saint Blaise quartier, located in the heart of authentic Paris with its flower lined café terraces, gardens and its air of rebellion, MAMA SHELTER welcomes you. Created by the Trigano family (co-founders of Club Med) and French philosopher Cyril Aouizerate, MAMA SHELTER was designed by Philippe Starck to offer an eclectic and electric ambiance. You'll find comfortable beds, with crazy bedside masks, huge Apple TV's and lots of neat touches to make your stay enjoyable.

At MAMA SHELTER you'll find sensual and elegant rooms equipped with iMacs and 5-star bedding to offer you a serene retreat after a long day in the city.

On the ground floor, a restaurant with simple family style dishes conceived by Alain Senderens, an enormous bar that also serves the purpose of being trendy, a brasserie, and a terrace where you might run into American rappers, Japanese painters, or Latin American writers. This space is not a prisoner to design. It's simple and functions as a cultural niche. There are several amusing elements in this space, and it's up to you to look for them and reflect on them. Have a seat in one of the armchairs near the chimney, which has been filled with illuminated candles yet to extinguish themselves. Hanging all along these common areas is an enormous curtain from which a crowd of happy faces looks out, arms outstretched, as if they are asking for an affectionate embrace from mankind. Who are the mama's on staff uniforms? What's written on the chalkboards on the ceilings? Lots of little jokes. Lots of little stories to be discovered.

LOCATION AND ACTIVITIES

In this upcoming bourgeoisie area, between the artists' studios, and the winding cobblestone streets, you will feel the lingering spirit of Edith Piaf, Oscar Wilde, Jim Morrison and other great artists. A blank canvas for you.

"Frivolous Philippe Starck design"

MAMA SHELTER
109 Rue de Bagnolet
Paris
75020
France
www.GoUnusual.com/MAMASHELTER

• Breakfast buffet available

LE CHÂTEAU D'ORFEUILLETTE
19TH CENTURY RESIDENCE REDECORATED IN MODERN STYLE

In the heart of 30 acres of Gévaudan parkland stands Château d'Orfeuillette, a 19th Century jewel. Recently redecorated with bold modern art themes, guests to the Château will feel as if they're part of an elaborate fairy tale. Although you're nestled in the historical setting of an ancient château, you'll find modern facilities, outdoor pool and gourmet dining with amazing dishes to tempt the palate.

Rooms are stunningly original, brightly coloured and full of excitement, elaborately decorated in a very modern style with those in the main chateau, spacious and bold.

White leather lounge seats in bay windows, rocking and bubble chairs in rooms. While you look out to an expanse of green grass and parkland, your senses will be on guard as the rooms aren't what you'd expect in a traditional property.

LOCATION AND ACTIVITIES

Le Château d'Orfeuillette is just off the main A75 motorway, is located a 1-hour drive from Clermont-Ferrand.

With wine advice of Thomas, the Château's sommelier, you can discover the wonders of the Languedoc wine region.

Indoor pool, SPA, sauna and hamam facilities are available outside the château in the nearby village.

"Be ready for nice surprises"

Le Chateau d'Orfeuillette
La Garde
Albaret Ste Marie
Languedoc-Roussillon 48200
France
www.GoUnusual.com/ChateaudOrfeuillette

• Boutique Property
• Gourmet restaurant

HÔTEL LE DONJON

EMBEDDED IN THE CITY WALLS OF UNESCO HERITAGE SITE

Hôtel le Donjon has grown as buildings were added around the central Château Comtal, in which the lords of Carcassonne had lived for years before the Cathar war saw their end.

The original owner of the 18 room Hôtel le Donjon was the father-in-law of current General Manager, Christine Pujol. Following the purchase of an adjoining house in the 1980's, itself part of an ancient orphanage, the original hotel started to expand. The family later bought adjoining hotel, les Remparts, a former mansion with magnificent sightseeing on the roofs and streets of the Medieval Citadel of Carcassonne, and in 2003, another private house joined to bring the hotel to it's current 61 rooms.

Some rooms are decorated with exposed stones and some with contemporary decor. All share views over the towers of the city or the tree-planted garden. At the warmest times of the day, you can linger in this garden, redolent with Mediterranean scents, or on the establishment's beautiful terrace.

LOCATION AND ACTIVITIES

As soon as one enters the Citadel, the medieval stones share stories of their history, but guests with the privilege to sleep in a real Medieval Citadel don't have to expect a Medieval welcome.

Each of the different houses has its own history and own piece of charm : les Remparts has a medieval stair with irregular stoned steps, le Donjon has a quiet garden which invites rest after having visited the Citadel and its surroundings, and le Comte Roger, the charm of being a private house.

"Sleep in a medieval citadel"

Hôtel le Donjon
2-4, rue du Comte Roger
Carcassonne
Languedoc 11000
France
www.GoUnusual.com/HotelleDonjon

• Boutique Property
• Breakfast provided
• Bar and Restaurant on site

CHÂTEAU DE FLOURE
ROMAN VILLA, THEN MONASTERY, NOW CHARMING HOTEL

Starting life as a Roman Villa on the Via Aquitania between Narbonne and Toulouse, in the middle ages the property became a monastery. Ten centuries after, during the reign of Henry IV, a president of the parliament of Toulouse made this his country retreat. As Château de Floure, it was then home of contemporary writer Gaston Bonheur (1913 – 1980).

The original character of this magical site was preserved when it was restored and converted to the current hotel, retaining the serenity of the formal gardens and developing the excellence of the restaurant "Le Poète Disparu".

Each of the 22 rooms of the property has modern comforts, but with their own style and charm. There are rooms and suites in the main building, with a couple of annexe buildings Les Hirondelles and Gaston Bonheur that are quieter, with views of the gardens.

Two suites are dedicated to lovers for a moment of romance.

Also, three large suites are available for families, sleeping up to four guests.

LOCATION AND ACTIVITIES

Château de Floure is very close to the Medieval City of Carcassonne - only 10 minutes by car or taxi.

The region is famous for the many Cathar Castles and Abbeys in the Aude region.

It is also possible to arrange a cruise on the nearby Canal du Midi.

There is an outdoor swimming pool and tennis court *available for hotel guests. A fully equipped spa is available for relaxation with indoor swimming pool, jacuzzi, hamam and sauna.*

"Where once a writer found inspiration, perhaps you'll find tranquility"

Château de Floure
1 rue Gaston Bonheur
Floure
Languedoc-Roussillon 11800
France
www.GoUnusual.com/ChateaudeFloure

• Boutique property
• Excellent restaurant

Languedoc-Roussillon,
take an exclusive break in Southern France

Follow the path to your exclusive holiday that won't compromise on luxury.

The Cercle Prestige is a selection of the very finest tourism sites Languedoc-Roussillon has to offer.

www.sunfrance.com/prestige

"A journey is best measured in friends, rather than miles."

Tim Cahill

LES JARDINS DE SAINT BENOIT
RESORT STYLED AROUND VINES AND VINEYARD COTTAGES

Surrounded by the beauty of the Corbières region - century old olive groves and vineyards, Les Jardins de Saint Benoît conceals a number of faithful updates to traditional "maisons vigneronnes", (winemaker's homes) and village houses. They offer from one to five bedrooms on both B&B and self catering format, with an outdoor pool for children and an indoor spa for adults.

Interiors are well proportioned, light and styled to provide a blend of traditional French elegance and contemporary calm. Each property opens out onto a private terrace, and 21 of the houses have the added luxury of a private swimming pool. With its squares, shaded fountains and restored walled medieval vegetable gardens, Les Jardins de Saint-Benoît blends naturally within the Languedoc landscape.

Aimed at nature and food lovers, as well as those keen to enjoy this special region, the village has pedestrian cobbled streets, fountains, olive groves, and an elegant pool area.

Younger children can visit the animals at the petting zoo while older children can go fly fishing in the local river or prepare the vegetables they picked in the medieval garden. Adults will enjoy the Spa and tennis facilities as well as organised food and wine tasting from local producers.

LOCATION AND ACTIVITIES

By road, St Laurent is about 10 minutes South of the A61 motorway. To get to Saint Laurent exit at Junction 25 (Lezignan-Corbières) then follow the signs to Fabrezan and then to Saint Laurent de Cabrerisse.

For your leisure time, the estate offers an indoor and outdoor heated pool, two tennis courts, a multi-sport facility, cooking lessons and sport coaching. The Kids Club welcomes children to enjoy activities on site, discovery tours of nature, the vegetable garden and the animal farm.

Take a dip in the swimming pool, indulge in a herb massage or participate in unpretentious wine tastings. Or, simply spend precious moments with your family while enjoying an array of landscapes and shared moments, that will make you reminisce of the France of yesteryear, of a universal and timeless sense of solace and peace.

"Sample a slower life in vineyard villages"

Les Jardins de Saint Benoit
Saint Laurent de la Cabrerrisse
Near Narbonne
Languedoc 11220
France
www.GoUnusual.com/LesJardinsdeSaintBenoit

• Vacation Rental
• Min stay 2 nights
• Suitable for Groups
• Self catering facilities

CHÂTEAU DE LASTOURS
VILLAS IN VINEYARD RALLY COURSE PROPERTY

Taken over by the Allard family in 2004, Château de Lastours was once known as "Castrum de Turribus", because of its location on the ancient Via Domitia linking Narbonne to Spain. Originally serving as an inn for travellers along this road through the heart of the Corbières, the 800 hectares of the estate include a 100-hectare vineyard, which produces a range of prestige wines.

Tucked between the vineyards and the moorland tracks you'll find the villas "Laurède" and "Aladers". With contemporary decor and quality furnishings their 12 rooms are an elegant setting from which to enjoy nature, cross country motorsport experiences - and the fine wines of the Château.

Rooms in the two villas all have private bathroom, air conditioning, mini bar, TV, and wireless internet.

LOCATION AND ACTIVITIES

Château de Lastours, with vines growing on terraces on the steep hillsides between the blue sky and the sea, overlooked by it's 300-metre high peak, is a remarkable site.

Enjoy and share the Allard family love of wine. Discover the quality and reputation of the great wines of the Château de Lastours whilst admiring the works featured in the annual summer exhibition in their wine cellar. Consider as well "La Bergerie" gourmet restaurant.. It is open all year and offers the perfect accompaniment to Château de Lastours wines, with its blend of Mediterranean produce and contemporary tastes.

The Château offers a number of vine themed activities: tasting, cellar visits, gourmet restaurants, seminars, groups and motorsport themed leisure activities.

The Château is regularly used as a testing ground for 4x4 vehicles and motorsport teams, it is a welcome stop on the Paris Dakar rally. Whether as a passenger in a 4x4 or at the wheel of a quadbike, explore Château de Lastours and its vineyards, along the routes used by competitors in the famed race.

"A terroir for fine wine and tuning rally cars"

Château de Lastours
Portel des Corbières
Languedoc 11490
France
www.GoUnusual.com/ChateaudeLastours

• Self Catering Villas
• Bar / Restaurant on site

CHÂTEAU L'HOSPITALET
THEMED ROOMS IN AWARD WINNING WINE ESTATE

With 82 hectares of vines and 1000 hectares of garrigue scrubland as far as the eye can see, Château l'Hospitalet provides a haven of peace, where the Mediterranean Art-de-Vivre strongly features.

It has 29 personalized rooms and 9 Suites, offering a thoroughly modern level of comfort. Every room takes notes from a different Gérard Bertrand wine - or from his other passions of Rugby and Jazz, and a bottle of specially chosen room-theme wine is available for guests to taste at their leisure.

Rooms look out over the vineyard vines or garden and have all the modern facilities you'd expect, including hairdryer, TV with cable and satellite, free wifi etc.

There are rooms and styles for all tastes and budgets.

The modest Classique room, with an agreeable and cosy design, are popular with those on a budget.

Guests arriving for a special occasion will appreciate Collection and Deluxe rooms or Suites.

LOCATION AND ACTIVITIES

Château l'Hospitalet is located in Narbonne, one of the oldest vine growing regions in the world and a land full of art and history. The city enjoys a strategic location, near to the Spanish border and the medieval city of Carcassonne.

It is 5 minutes drive from the Mediterranean coast - for beaches, coastal walks, cafes and restaurants. Château l'Hospitalet is ideally situated to share the lifestyles of both vine and sea.

The gourmet Restaurant is led by chef, Christophe Arthur, with delicious food matched to wines.

"Ideally situated to blend both cork and coast"

Château l'Hospitalet
Route de Narbonne Plage
Narbonne
Languedoc 11 100
France
www.GoUnusual.com/ChateaulHospitalet

• Boutique Property
• Gourmet restaurant

CHÂTEAU DE RAISSAC
200 YEAR OLD WINE ESTATE BEDROOMS

Joseph Barthélémy Viennet acquired the Château de Raissac on the 15th of July 1828. Today, owners Christine and Jean Viennet share rooms in their Château with guests while their son Gustave and his wife Marie continue 200 years of wine making tradition.

In a warm atmosphere and wonderful surroundings, dinners are prepared by your host with the ingredients of the vegetable garden. Jean Viennet cooks with care and creativity following the day's inspiration - in harmony with the wines of the estate.

On the first floor, the five comfortable bedrooms combine elegance and charm. Each room has its own style and story, furnished with antiques, cues of art deco styling and paintings from the 19th and the 20th centuries. Spacious and bright, with en-suite bathrooms and toilets, they all overlook the beautiful garden.

LOCATION AND ACTIVITIES

The Château de Raissac is located near the river Orb, 3 kms North of Béziers, in the heart of the province of Languedoc.

Christine, a renowned ceramist, has founded a Museum of Ceramics and of 19th century Arts de la Table in the beautiful old stables. Jean, a painter invites you to discover his portraits and murals in the Château.

Guests can relax in a peaceful garden and enjoy delicious dinners served under majestic trees facing the charming

19th century greenhouse, or in the shade of the bamboos, more intimately, in the smaller 17th century dining room.

"Magical and historic setting"

Château de Raissac
Route de Murviel (D19)
Béziers
Languedoc 34500
France
www.GoUnusual.com/ChateaudeRaissac

• Bed and Breakfast
• Inspired cooking by the owner
available

CHÂTEAU DE MONTCAUD

CHÂTEAU OF THE ELEGANT AND SOBER STYLE OF NAPOLEON III PERIOD

It is difficult to imagine anything at once restful and more stimulating than the stay which Anne and Rudy Baur offer their guests at Château de Montcaud. What was once an overrun and empty property for 20 years, has been restored to former glory by the Baur family who purchased it in 1992. Retaining the charm of it's origin as a 19th Century family in splendid parkland, the Château keeps it's homely feel with unobtrusive but attentive service.

Owner Rudy W. Baur, an alumni of the Lausanne hotel school, puts into practice the lessons from many years of hospitality experience. Following it's purchase, Rudy and wife Anne manage Chateau de Montcaud as a family enterprise with a special personal welcome.

Your entry through the gate is flanked by plane trees leading to the majestic and romantic park, left natural and kept to the original plans of 1892. In the old Mas are located the reception, the restaurant and meeting rooms.

The 27 rooms offer all the comfort you could wish for, offering a rest and disconnect from the daily routine.

LOCATION AND ACTIVITIES

On the outskirts of Bagnols-sur-Cèze, 30min North of Avignon, Château de Montcaud lies at the crossroads of legendary cultural and historic sites - Pont-du Gard, Nîmes, Avignon and the Roman theatre in Orange where the annual Opera-Festival is also the highlight of Montcaud's summer season. It is the perfect departure point from which to discover this beautiful region.

Enjoy the pleasures of the home from home, its Mediterranean cuisine and the nearby attractions of Provence's historic towns and neighbouring Côtes-du-Rhône vineyards.

"You will be happy here.
Leaving is the only difficulty"

Château de Montcaud
Hameau de Combe-Sabran
Sabran
Languedoc 30200
France
www.GoUnusual.com/ChateaudeMontcaud

• Boutique Property
• Bar / Restaurant on site

HOSTELLERIE LE CASTELLAS
GOURMET DINING WITH THEMED ROOMS

In 1989, the APARIS family restored a set of three buildings from the 17th century in the old medieval village of Collias to create Hostellerie le Castellas. Combining a vision to bring life once again to a collection of undervalued buildings, they also chose to inject a welcome sense of fun to the development, as well as introduce world class dining.

Now perfectly restored, the buildings are arranged around a luxurious patio transformed into an exotic garden. A pool resembling a Roman bath is concealed below. Peaceful and luxurious, the 20 air conditioned rooms each bear an individual style - art deco, art nouveau, art contemporary, 1970s. Modern facilities in a traditional setting.

The dining experience is special and merits it's 2 star Michelin award. While fine ingredients are the foundation, it is delicious without being pretentious, and a reason to visit on its own. Check out their special events and day-courses.

LOCATION AND ACTIVITIES

Hostellerie Castellas is in the heart of the village of Collias, in the gorges of the Gardon, between Nîmes and Avignon. With easy access by Eurostar, flights or car, it makes a fantastic romance location for couples. The "Alpilles", "Camargue" and "Cévennes", between the "Pont du Gard" and Uzès are all within easy reach by car.

Food is an important theme in this blend of old and new. Breakfast can be taken under the wisteria on the terrace. In the evening, perhaps the hushed atmosphere of the garden with its subdued lights, or in one of the vaulted rooms of

the restaurant, you can savour Jérôme Nutile's inventive food. His Two Michelin star cuisine, served with wines chosen by the sommelier, Jean-Luc Sauron are reasons enough to visit. Stays can additionally be accompanied by a wide range of sporting activities and, for gourmands, cooking lessons and special ingredient theme events.

"Blending history, style and gourmet experiences"

Hostellerie le Castellas
30, Grand 'Rue
Collias
Languedoc 30210
France
www.GoUnusual.com/HostellerieleCastellas

• Boutique Property
• 2* Michelin restaurant

DOMAINE DES ESCAUNES

HISTORIC ESTATE, ONCE VISITED BY ROYALTY AND NOBLEMEN

An ancient Royal hostelry dating from the 16th Century and restored in the finest tradition, nestling among the vines and olive trees.

From its origin in the 16th century (1537), the Domaine was a Royal hostelry – staging post, where "Francis the First" and his second wife "Eleanor of Austria", "Catherine de Medici" and the future King "Henri IV" as well as "Louis XIII" accompanied by Cardinal Richelieu, had sleeping accommodation. In 1564, King Charles IX spent a night in his carriage parked in the courtyard.

The chronicle of Michel de Nostredame, better known under his Latin name Nostradamus, suggests he stayed a few days in the inn.

The rooms have been recently renovated, each with unique décor. Rooms have their own bathroom, some of them with a bath imitating the styles of an earlier period in a baroque decor, others with big Italian showers in a mellow atmosphere. There are arched ceilings in some cases, mouldings in others, with each room well furnished with quality fittings.

The combination of the traditional hospitality offered by owners Marc and Patricia Vermeulen and avant-garde furnishing makes for a memorable venue in a fantastic area.

LOCATION AND ACTIVITIES

Close to Avignon, Nîmes, Uzès and Arles, you are centrally located to visit the many cities of culture and tradition of Provence, and also to sample the delicious regional food.

The grounds of the property have not only outdoor pool facilities, but enclosed, private space for families to share time together.

**"Offering hospitality, style and modernity
- in a great location"**

Domaine des Escaunes
5 Rue des Bourgades
Sernhac
Languedoc 30210
France
www.GoUnusual.com/DomainedesEscaunes

• Boutique Property
• Fantastic for family groups and celebrations

307

Europe

Spain, Portugal, Andorra

Key
Entries in **Bold** typeface indicate full page entries with a photo.
Others are additional indexed entries.

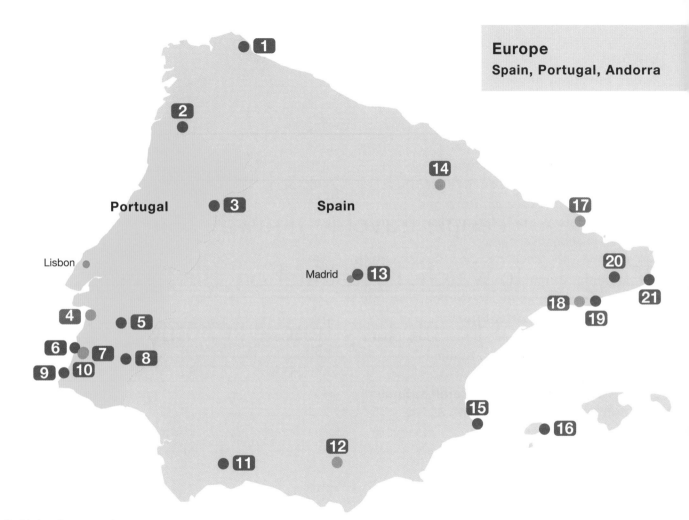

Europe
Spain, Portugal, Andorra

Portugal

Spain

Lisbon

Madrid

1

2

3

14

17

13

20

4

5

18

19

21

6

7

8

9

10

15

16

12

11

● Main photo entries
● Address entries

"People travel to faraway places
to watch, in fascination, the kind
of people they ignore at home."

Dagobert D. Runes

MONTE CHORA CASCAS
ROOMS THEMED AROUND GUARDIAN ANGELS

Opened in 1999, Monte Chora Cascas has established itself as one of Portugal's most highly regarded country homes open to guests.

The house, with six individually decorated double rooms themed on Guardian Angels, lies on a gently rounded ridge overlooking a valley of olive and cork groves, with the hilltop castle of Montemor-o-Novo on the horizon.

LOCATION AND ACTIVITIES

Just one hour's drive from Lisbon, the Monte offers easy access to the outdoor beauty of the Alentejo region. Explore them on foot, by bicycle, on horseback – or from the basket of a hot-air balloon.

The municipality of Montemor-o-Novo has turned a disused local railway line into a bicycle and walking trail, the Ecopista do Montado. It offers perhaps the easiest way of experiencing the nature of the Alentejo. Ask about bicycle rentals for an outing among cork oaks and olive trees.

"To enjoy this earthly paradise is to realise that heaven can wait..."

Monte Chora Cascas
Apartado 296
Montemor-o-Novo
Alentejo 7050-013
Portugal
www.GoUnusual.com/MonteChoraCascas

CASA DA CISTERNA

LUXURIOUS B&B IN FORTIFIED VILLAGE FILLED WITH HISTORY

Casa da Cisterna is a fabulously restored guest house on several levels in the historical village of Castelo Rodrigo. The town is named after the ruined castle and surrounded by ancient walls with views across the Douro Valley and to Spain.

Seduced and fascinated by the charms of rural life in Castelo Rodrigo, owners Ana and António have converted once ruined buildings next to the ancient water cistern for the village, giving rise to the Casa da Cisterna name. As well as beautifully decorated rooms and cool stone walls, the uppermost terrace has a plunge pool where spectacular views reach far across the roofs of the town to the distant plateau beyond.

The six double rooms and suite of Casa da Cisterna are all named after local birds and very comfortable. Decorated differently, they reflect the personal taste of the owners, making you feel immediately at home. Light colours and cosy decorations used throughout rooms and common areas give a sense of comfort and simplicity.

Beautifully restored across a number of terrace levels, the house has a small garden on the top, where sun loungers are ideally situated for sunny weather. Garden rooms are quieter and a good option in colder months, having the warmth of an individual fireplace. The uppermost terrace has the plunge pool, where you're surrounded by a fantastic view across the roofs of the village every evening.

LOCATION AND ACTIVITIES

Casa da Cisterna is located in a very interesting region, rich in landscape, history and nature. Nearby are other Historical Villages and also the Douro Internacional Natural Park and its great landscapes.

While there is only a small terrace in Casa da Cisterna, with pool and stunning South facing views, the real backyard is the village itself. Full of interesting things to see, every doorway is filled with character.

"Fortified walls share centuries of history"

Casa da Cisterna
Castelo Rodrigo
Beira Alta
Portugal
www.GoUnusual.com/CasadaCisterna

• Bed & Breakfast
• Restaurants nearby

313

"The traveler sees what he sees.
The tourist sees what he has
come to see."

GK Chesterton

CASA DO RIO VEZ
IDYLLIC RIVERSIDE MILL NOW STYLISHLY RENOVATED

LOCATION AND ACTIVITIES

The clean and clear River Vez flows alongside, renowned not only for excellent trout, but for swimming and waterside picnics. The property doesn't serve dinner or lunch, but there are several restaurants in nearby Arcos de Valdavez 2,5km away, and other food choices in nearby Ponte da Barca or Ponte de Lima - including many by the riverside.

You're in a relatively unspoilt and under developed region, with fantastic scenery and natural resources for walking, including some of the best sandy beaches of Northern Portugal.

"Idyllic riverside retreat, with stylish fittings"

This ancient riverside olive oil mill dates back to 1886, now stylishly converted to provide 4 well furnished B&B bedrooms and a spacious self catering loft apartment. With a double height dining room and windows for all rooms facing the river, you can see owner Anibal's architectural expertise. He and his wife Valerie are excellent, attentive hosts. There is also a pool to help work off the excellent breakfast, with fresh breads, cereals, local cheeses, charcuterie and home made preserves.

Casa Do Rio Vez,
Couto
Arcos de Valdevez
4970-130
Portugal
www.GoUnusual.com/CasaDoRioVez

"Do we really want to travel in hermetically sealed popemobiles through the rural provinces of France, Mexico and the Far East, eating only in Hard Rock Cafes and McDonalds? Or do we want to eat without fear, tearing into the local stew, the humble taqueria's mystery meat, the sincerely offered gift of a lightly grilled fish head? I know what I want. I want it all. I want to try everything once."

Anthony Bourdain, Kitchen Confidential: Adventures in the Culinary Underbelly

MALHADINHA NOVA
VINEYARD WITH DESIGN HOTEL AND SPA

LOCATION AND ACTIVITIES

The conversion of a rustic farm into a luxurious, boutique property blends with the beautiful rolling landscape of the vast Alentejo plain.

A spa and pool nestling among the vineyards, spacious elegant rooms - and gourmet food and wine.

The restaurant offers a cuisine with modern interpretations of traditional dishes favouring local produce.

"Experience passion for Wine and Life!"

Malhadinha Nova - Vineyard & Spa
Albernoa
Beja
Portugal
www.GoUnusual.com/MalhadinhaNova-VineyardandSpa

This vineyard and country house property is a chic haven with designer furnished rooms and three superb suites for comfort and peace. A spa and top restaurant, featuring wines from their own vineyards in the winelist, completes the picture.

The combination of design, country living, comfort and elegance that Malhadinha Nova offers is sure to appeal to your senses and feelings.

"Not all those who wander are lost."

– J. R. R. Tolkien

MUXIMA - MONTES FERREIROS
THEMED RURAL B+B

LOCATION AND ACTIVITIES

Respecting the traditional local architecture, Muxima has two buildings. One is constructed of "taipa" and the other is made of iron stone. Of the seven rooms, four are apartments that can accommodate larger groups with additional beds. Located in a protected wild forest area, 28 hectares of cork-trees and arbutus surround to keep nature intact and wild.

The property is only 6km from the beautiful beaches of the Atlantic Ocean and near one of the best surf spots in Europe (like Arrifana or Amado).

"Try the Muxima biological pool with its natural plants and resident frogs!"

This boutique B&B has rooms themed around countries of the owners travels and has a rural, rustic location within a protected natural park. Muxima means 'heart' in the Angolan dialect and here you'll feel a relaxed African ambiance inspired by exotic trips.

Muxima
Montes Ferreiros
Aljezur
Algarve 8670-000
Portugal
www.GoUnusual.com/MuximaMontesFerreiros

319

NESPEREIRA ESTATE - MOINHO DE VENTO
WINDMILL IN CORK ESTATE

Nespereira is a privately owned rural estate set high in the Alentejo National Ecological Reserve, 15km inland from the coast. Up on the top of the hill, the Moinho de Vento (Windmill) has spectacular views of rolling hills and distant mountains. This romantic rental property is perfect for a couple looking for a unique location, luxury accommodation and distinctive surroundings. Whilst the mezzanine bedroom is cosy, large windows on either side expand the feeling of space and light, and there is a generous modern kitchen and large marble bathroom which includes a walk-in shower, basin and WC.

There are also sunloungers available and in winter the wood burning stove provides a romantic focal point in the living room which is also equipped with MP3 speakers.

LOCATION AND ACTIVITIES

The nearest airport to the Alentejo and the Nespereira Estate is Faro in Southern Portugal. Bordering Spain in the north and the Algarve in the south, this region is an untouched rural escape from the bustling cities of the Atlantic coast.

Whilst one of the main attractions of the accommodation at The Nespereira Estate are their seclusion and privacy, the owners appreciate that shared amenities are important. They therefore created a 15m Swimming Pool and a beautifully landscaped terrace complete with sun loungers and tables. The pool benefits from spectacular views and a cooling breeze.

The Alentejo is renowned for its stunning natural beauty, with nature reserves throughout the region preserving the landscape. In particular, the southwest coastline, the Costa Vincente offers visitors magnificent, sparsely populated beaches, which are treated as a protected area to ensure the preservation of miles of beautiful sandy shores.

The South-west coast is home to some of the best surfing in the world and the area's nature parks offer visitors a chance to explore on horseback, mountain bikes or foot.

"An undiscovered haven in Portugal that is unspoilt and unique"

Nespereira Estate
Casa Nova da Cruz
Odemira
Alentego, 9630000
Portugal
www.GoUnusual.com/Nespereira Estate

• Vacation Rental properties
• Self catering
• Bar / Cafe on site

CABANES ALS ARBRES
TREEHOUSES IN FOREST SETTING

Rediscover your childhood dreams and live in a cabin in the treetops hanging 10m above the ground attached to the trunks of robust Douglas firs. The first two treehouses opened in July 2009, and today there are ten - six 2-person cabins and four 4-person cabins.

Owners Karin and Manu have a clear idea of the site's philosophy:

"Our goal is to offer the pleasure of spending a night with a tree and its ecosystem, while teaching people about the importance of the environment."

Once checked in, you're overcome by the feeling of living a childhood adventure. The cabins are built in the trees of Montseny and have no ground supports. They are supported by several cables to divide the weight. Entrance is by a suspended bridge or a ladder.

Sadly the resort cannot accommodate children younger than 10 years old.

All the cabins are made from wood, (even the handles on the windows), and are built around the tree. The room space is 30 m² with an additional 10 m² of terrace. The interior, through which the trunk passes vertically, is furnished with a double bed, sofa, table and chairs; there's a "bathroom" area with jugs of water and a dry toilet. The treehouses have no electricity, (Karin and Manu provide candles and torches) and no running water. However, a short distance away at Mas La Vileta, (which also offers rooms), is the reception area where all amenities are located, including showers, toilets, a magnificent swimming pool and restaurant.

LOCATION AND ACTIVITIES

At the heart of the Sierra del Montseny, 84 km (52 miles) from Barcelona,

"Don't forget to bring warm clothes
- You're in the mountains!"

Cabanes als Arbres
Sant Hilari Sacalm
Girona 17403
Spain
www.GoUnusual.com/CabanesalsArbres

• Breakfast provided
• Children over 10 only admitted
• Restaurants nearby

323

EL CASTAÑO DORMILÓN

RESTORED OLD SCHOOL IN HERITAGE REGION OF NATURAL BEAUTY

The El Castaño Dormilón building is a restored old village school, converted to a beautiful house reflecting the simplicity of the Rías Altas natural reserve. From the Horse Chestnuts in lamps to the ecological energy systems, owners Mónica and Alex provide a great base for those exploring this largely untouched region of Galicia, one hour and ten minutes away from A Coruña and one hour and 40 minutes from Santiago de Compostela!

LOCATION AND ACTIVITIES

Located in the heart of Rías Altas in Galicia, an area that remains wild, untouched and away from human intervention.

It is a fantastic place. Lush coastal vegetation. Stunning scenery. Fine sandy beaches.

Only 20 minutes from the property you can visit the magnificent scenery between the highest cliffs in continental Europe at Cape Ortegal, (mythical place where the Atlantic ocean meets the Cantabrian sea), and Estaca de Bares, the most northerly point of Spain.

Nearby, bird watchers will want to visit the Ladrido Ramsar reserve, protected because of its high ornithological value for migrating and coastal birds.

If you love surfing you must go to Pantin (35 minutes away) which hosts the world championships. It's up to you!.

"Back to school and back to nature"

El Castaño Dormilón
Baleo 15, Ortigueira
A Coruna, Galicia 15339
Spain
www.GoUnusual.com/ElCastanoDormilon

• Bed & Breakfast
• Restaurants nearby

HOTEL ENFRENTE ARTE

CRAZY HOME WITH FUN, FUNKY TOUCHES AND FISH PEDICURE

EnfrenteArte is a bohemian, alternative, funky bed and breakfast hotel, decorated with eclectic details, original and historical artwork and atmospheric lighting. A Fiat 600 in reception - why not! There are lots of fun and funky touches. Lights and birds nesting in old basketballs. Wall murals of Michael Jackson and Freddie Mercury. Car tyres converted to occasional tables. A surfboard dining table. Plus quality amenities and helpful hosts.

For those enjoying Ronda on foot, you'll appreciate the complimentary "Doctor Fish" pedicure, as well as a sauna, outdoor pool and jacuzzi.During your stay, all drinks, breakfast and the use of all facilities are included in the price of the room.

LOCATION AND ACTIVITIES

This 3-star hotel was created with the idea of being an extension of your home - without rules, schedules and with free access to every single part of the hotel during the day.

Enfrente Arte has 12 double rooms of different types, each with its own character and individual design. Some offer romantic courtyards or terraces with views of the mountains, the river 'Guadalevin', the old city or the renowned horse riding school 'Maestranza de Ronda'.

As well as all the quirky art touches, rooms have a private bathroom, television with Canal Plus, Sky TV and free movie channels, telephone, central heating and air-conditioning.

The included breakfast is available until midday, which is especially welcome for those who've enjoyed a Spanish-

style late night dinner and entertainment in the local bars and hostelries.

Included in the room price is the Enfrente Arte self service bar which offers a selection of tea, coffee, natural juices, beer and different wines. You can also sample the "Doctor Fish" pedicure treatment and have access to all hotel facilities including Jacuzzi, sauna and outdoor pool.

Beautifully situated in the oldest paved street of Ronda and surrounded by historic buildings, this unique and laid back hotel is located a few minutes away from the city centre facing the natural park 'Sierra de las Nieves'.

"A lot of fun"

Hotel Enfrente Arte
Calle Real, 42
Ronda,
Andalucia 29400
Spain
www.GoUnusual.com/EnfrenteArte

• Breakfast provided
• Restaurants nearby

HOTEL PUERTA AMERICA
A DIFFERENT DESIGN EXPERIENCE ON EVERY FLOOR

With 12 floors and communal spaces providing a unique style designed by 19 design agencies, your choice of room is critical at Hotel Puerta América. Thankfully the front desk staff anticipate guests changing rooms. A menu of design choices for the different floors is provided at check-in and you are recommended to study closely, or to review the website in advance. Some floors are a triumph of style over substance and there are stories of guests whose frustration to dim the walls, or use hi-tech appliances forced them to change rooms. Although floors have a similar layout, when you exit the elevator on each floor you feel in altogether different worlds – from futuristic red plastic to black marble through to traditional leather and wood.

Example floors include the first floor by Zaha Hadid, where everything seems to come out from the wall. The bathroom is a single structure from floor to ceiling which changes colour according to the room. Most frustratingly the waste basket is intended as a challenge for guests, because it is not so easy to find. Or you can just drop your rubbish on the floor with frustration.

The eighth floor by Kathryn Findlay titled "Light in motion" intends to suggest a feminine touch. Refusing to consider walls or doors, Findley provided for sweeping white curtains that separate the bathroom from the room. The entire room is white and forms a single space.

Patience is required on the ninth floor of Richard Gluckman with his 'Boxes of colours' concept as you need to find everything in the room and bathroom, because it is hidden in a box. In the bathroom, the first thing you see when you enter the room, is a large glass box containing the shower, with a sliding door separating it from the bedroom by means of a white metal curtain. Contrasting a raw industrial look with back-lit illumination, it is critical for guests to ask how to turn off the lights, otherwise you'll struggle to get to sleep.

LOCATION AND ACTIVITIES

The hotel is midway between the airport and the city centre and is not in the centre of town. Be prepared to take a taxi into town for restaurants and entertainment. Alternatively consider the metro stop next to the hotel.

"A design adventure!"

Hotel Puerta América
Avenida de América, 41
Spain
www.GoUnusual.com/HotelPuertaAmerica

• Breakfast provided
• Bar / Restaurant on site

REFUGIO MARNES CASAS RURALES
BEDOUIN TENT, BARN CONVERSION AND B&B IN ECO REFUGE

LOCATION AND ACTIVITIES

Your hosts offer the opportunity to have meals on reservation with wine included. Do not miss the opportunity to sample their excellent cooking skills!

If you fly to Alicante, then travelling by car you can be at Refugio Marnes within one hour.

"Sun, peace, nature and history"

Refugio Marnes consists of a centuries old rural finca (estate) spanning 50 acres of agricultural land, situated in a private valley. The owners offer three options: the old farmhouse where the owners live with its B&B wing Los Establos, a cottage called La Ruina and finally, hidden in the countryside, the luxurious Moroccan Bedouin tent, "Jaima". Stylishly equipped for a comfortable and original holiday for 4 persons, the tent is set on a stone platform with a proper bathroom and kitchen. No more tripping over the guy-ropes of your neighbours. Instead you'll discover a spacious refuge with privacy and 50 acres of land for you to explore.

Refugio Marnes Casas Rurales
Ptd Marnes 20115
Benissa
Alicante
Spain
www.GoUnusual.com/RefugioMarnesCasasRurales

- Bed & Breakfast
- Vacation Rental
- Dinner by arrangement
- Self catering

HOSTAL SA RASCASSA
MILLIONAIRE HIDEAWAY IN SECLUDED COVE

No need to drive or wait for a taxi as your bedroom is just next door. Five great twin-bedded rooms, (beds can be put together), with bathroom en-suite, TV and heating – and no telephone! A common terrace with sea views and direct access to the cove. The sea – a rocky cove through the pines at Cala d'Aiguafreda - only 40 meters away.

Welcome to the idyllic retreat of Sa Rascassa, where a millionaire escaped the action of the Costa Brava, to enjoy the peace and tranquility of nature.

LOCATION AND ACTIVITIES

There is so much to see and do here:

Beautiful scenery (coves, beaches, countryside and the Pyrenees...), gastronomy, culture (medieval towns, 'Cuban' houses, Romanesque architecture, Greco-Roman ruins, Dali museum, exhibitions, music festivals...), and sports (golf, scuba diving, mountain biking, sailing, fishing, trekking...).

"The ingredients of happy memories and a great nights sleep"

Imagine a virtually uninhabited cove on the Costa Brava. A peaceful beachside restaurant on a beautiful evening. The sound of the sea your soundtrack to a candlelit meal of perfectly cooked, fresh local ingredients. Fantastic wine. A glass of brandy as the sun goes down.

Hostal Sa Rascassa
Cala d'Aiguafreda
Begur, Girona 17255
Spain
www.GoUnusual.com/HostalSaRascassa

RETROME, BARCELONA
VINTAGE STYLE FROM THE 1950S AND 60S

LOCATION AND ACTIVITIES

Carrer Girona is well connected and has good public transport links in the area. A metro stop (Girona) is just around the corner and less than two minutes walk away. You can reach the world famous "Passeo De Gracia" in 5 minutes on foot and "Plaça Catalunya" and "La Rambla" or the "Sagrada Familia" in about 10 minutes.

"Funky retro-chic design in the centre of a great city"

Combining original "modernista" features with great retro-vintage design, Retrome - Barcelona has museum worthy tiles at the entrance, art from the 50's and 60's in rooms and common areas, high (cool) ceilings, French windows in the front rooms and terraced rooms in the back.

Each room is different in design, yet equally offers the same high standard. In the comfortable lounge area you can find books, magazines, a large reading or conference table, tea making facilities and a vintage espresso machine for a dose of caffeine. A small yet delicious Spanish/Healthy menu breakfast is included.

Retrome - Barcelona
Carrer De Girona 85
Barcelona, Catalunia 08009
Spain
www.GoUnusual.com/Retrome-Barcelona

"A journey of a thousand miles

must begin with a single step."

Lao Tzu

USHUAÏA IBIZA BEACH HOTEL
AVANT-GARDE CONCEPT WITH CONTEMPORARY PERSONALITY

LOCATION AND ACTIVITIES

A large buffet breakfast is included during guests' stay, or they can opt for an a la carte breakfast* served in the Magic & Chill Garden, next to the pool.

People come to Ibiza to sample the nightlife and parties, although there is plenty to tempt those looking for a break from the music. The island has a mix of culture, crystal blue waters, warm weather, caves and markets. Highlights include the 14th century Cathedral and walls from the Renaissance - declared in 1999 a World Heritage Site.

"Beach party with style and substance"

The Ushuaïa Ibiza Beach Hotel is the ideal choice for those who come to Ibiza for the best beach & pool parties, with live performances of top DJs, and a day and night ambiance in a modern setting with all kinds of comforts and luxuries on one of the Islands most exciting beaches. Swimming pools, Balinese beds, a fashion boutique, a Spa and a fully equipped gym. A place where live DJ sessions take place weekly, as well as fashion shows, performances and more.

Ushuaïa Ibiza Beach Hotel
Carretera Playa d'en Bossa, 10
Sant Jordi de ses Salines
Ibiza 07817
Spain
www.GoUnusual.com/UshuaiaIbizaBeachHotel

Europe
Italy

Key
Entries in **Bold** typeface indicate full page entries with a photo.
Others are additional indexed entries.

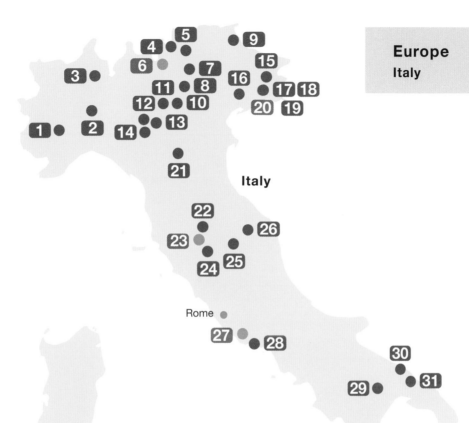

Europe

Italy

Italy

Rome

● Main photo entries

● Address entries

RELAIS CATTEDRALE
17TH CENTURY FRESCOES AND HANDMADE UNIQUE BEDS

atmosphere, highlighted by special period furniture combined with ethnic and modern elements. Each bed has been custom designed for each room.

LOCATION AND ACTIVITIES

Located in the centre of historic Asti, the Relais team are able to advise on trips and tours - as well as exhibitions and tourism ideas in the Piedmont region.

"Character and charm in the city of Asti"

The rooms are all based around Latin terms for spices and flavours - and the furnishings and colours underline the spice theme.

This property is an oasis of peace in the city center of the bustling, medieval city of Asti. It's warm and refined setting makes it the perfect start to your journey in the Monferrato and Piedmont's wine country - and for driving tours in this charming region of Italy.

All guests benefit from a scenic terrace, recreation room with TV, stereo and a large collection of Vinyl records. From June to October the hotel opens their Sound Garden "OSSIGENO", showcasing an Art Exhibition with appetizer.

Each of the six rooms and one suite, offers their own unique

Relais Cattedrale
Via Cattedrale, 7
Asti
Piemonte
Italy
www.GoUnusual.com/RelaisCattedrale

• Breakfast provided
• Restaurants nearby

MAISON MOSCHINO
DESIGNER FAIRYTALE INSPIRED ROOM THEMES

True to the essence of the Moschino brand, this classical Milan railway terminus building has been completely reinterpreted to offer 65 contemporary hotel rooms inspired by 16 different fairytale themes. Today, the exterior facade of Viale Monte Grappa 12 is a reminder of the station's original grandeur. Spread out across four floors, the rooms are sensuous visions of surreal diversity. Highly imaginative and eccentric, the Moschino design team created spaces to inspire the mind where fashion is king.

The connection between the rooms is that of a fairytale theme. From the rose strewn bed covering of Life is a Bed of Roses, to a four poster bed with trees in The Forest, or a bedridden wolf in Little Red Riding Hood. Entering the Maison Moschino is like falling down Lewis Carroll's Alice in Wonderland rabbit hole: after a while, you come to expect the unexpected!

The hotel features several luxurious amenities supporting the surreal Moschino theme. The ground floor bar serves dream inspired drinks, welcoming guests into the hotel. Located underground, the sub-level, Culti Spa is sublime, offering massage rooms, Turkish bath, jacuzzi and a cosy gym.

The imaginative "Clandestino Milano" restaurant created by chef Moreno Cedroni includes a gourmet Italian twist of Japanese sushi called 'Susci' – combining linguistic creativity with the finest Italian ingredients. Try also the Mos Kit breakfast, inspired by a shoebox, as a sensual special treat. Not only does it look fabulous, it tastes amazing.

LOCATION AND ACTIVITIES

Hotel Maison Moschino, is located in the vibrant and ever-evolving district near Corso Como and Corso Garibaldi in the heart of Milan, the Italian capital of business and fashion. All the city's main attractions are within easy reach.

"The restaurant is amazing"

Hotel Maison Moschino
Viale Monte Grappa 12
Milan
20124
Italy
www.GoUnusual.com/MaisonMoschino

• Breakfast provided
• Bar / Amazing restaurant

343

"Once in a while it really hits people that they don't have to experience the world in the way they have been told to."

Alan Keightley

Dressed for the occasion

ALESSI
The Useful Art

"Dressed". Table set, design Marcel Wanders, 2011.

CASA BRENNA TOSATTO
GALLERY PAYING HOMAGE TO INFLUENTIAL ARTIST

A Liberty Style House on Lake Como that is designated as an association devoted to art, totally redesigned as "chic enclave", with an intriguing mélange of contemporary and antique design and works of art distributed throughout the house. One apartment on three floors is dedicated to the artist Mario Tosatto, born in 1885 who created some remarkable works in his short 27 year lifespan.

LOCATION AND ACTIVITIES

The Casa Brenna Tosatto has a total of 4 self-catering units and can also be rented out individually or in its entirety, hosting up to 15 guests. The casa represents an island for art, located in a place of great natural beauty, an ideal place to spend a restful break, meditating, creating or even just relaxing and (re)discovering the splendor of Lake Como, just a short drive from Milan. The owner can offer suggestions on a boating trip on the lake, cooking courses or secret trattorias frequented by the locals.

Casa Brenna Tosatto
Via Mattia del Riccio 3
Campo di Lenno
Lombardia 22016
Italy
www.GoUnusual.com/CasaBrennaTosatto

- Vacation Rental
- Group bookings
- Self catering facilties

347

IMPERIAL ART HOTEL
DESIGNER ROOMS IN HISTORIC SETTING

LOCATION AND ACTIVITIES

VIP access to the famous Merano Thermal baths designed by Matteo Thun is included in room prices. The baths are 200m from the hotel.

Although the hotel doesn't have a restaurant they have a prestigious coffee house with a signature South Tyrol Coffee "Schreyögg", snack bar with sandwiches and cold snacks. The favourite aperitif in the bar is the famous "Hugo" with Prosecco, fresh mint, lemon squeeze and elder syrup.

Serving discerning wealthy and famous visitors at the healing spas of Merano for over a century, the centrally located Imperial Art Hotel partners the spa and offers beautiful Art suites that combine comfort, art and lifestyle.

No two suites are the same and the three Merano based designers have created modern interior design, in a stunning centuries old setting, to create something stunning that Merano has never seen

"Where hospitality and art seamlessly intertwine"

Imperial Art Hotel
Corso libertá
Merano, Südtirol 39012
Italy
www.GoUnusual.com/ImperialArtHotel

- Breakfast provided
- Bar / Restaurant on site

349

MEISTERS HOTEL IRMA
TREEHOUSE SUITE IN LUXURY HOTEL

LOCATION AND ACTIVITIES

South Tyrol is the province in gourmet-country Italy with the highest concentration of award-winning wines and Michelin starred restaurants – thanks perhaps to the large choice of wines, fruit, cheeses and asparagus. In Merano the passion for fine foods is a way of life, and this shows in the sheer number of special gourmet places.

To work up an appetite - or work off previous visits(!), you will find endless hiking possibilities such as the Maiser Waalweg trail or the high altitude farm trail. A true hiking paradise, there are a great variety of routes for all skill levels leading through untouched forests.

"Amazing for honeymoon and romantic proposals"

Effortlessly integrated in the mighty pines this spacious treehouse suite combines luxury and nature, with a bed that can be moved onto the balcony for a complete open air experience, or simply to enjoy the superb South Tyrolian scenery. Even the bathtub has a fantastic view!

The adjoining main building of the Meisters Hotel Irma is both a gourmet and spa/wellness destination in its own right with many trips and activities to enjoy in the area by bicycle, on foot or with a gourmet guide.

Meisters Hotel Irma
Belvedere 19
Merano / Meran, I-39012
Italy
www.GoUnusual.com/MeistersHotelIrma

- Breakfast provided
- Bar / Restaurant on site

MIRAMONTI BOUTIQUE HOTEL
ROMANCE IN THE SILENT FOREST

LOCATION AND ACTIVITIES

Miramonti coined the term "Forest Therapy". Klaus will hide your smartphone then take you for a walk in the woods where he shows you relaxation techniques and helps you "listen" to the silence and commune with the trees.

"It sounds very new age, but I have had stressed-out top managers thank me for helping them disconnect and learn how powerful silence is", says Klaus.

"Listen to the sound of silence"

To enter the gates of Miramonti, you press a button and say the secret password. You drive up the ramp to the entrance and as soon as you walk in, you feel something different.

Klaus and Carmen are in love, and Miramonti is their baby. This alpine lodge is intimate and welcoming, modern and toasty warm. And it holds quite a few surprises, like the loft room with its own telescope, so you can look down on the twinkling valley of Merano far below, or gaze up at the planets and stars above you.

Rooms are inspired by the beauty of nature. Open the window and experience the impressive tranquility and the beautiful view on the cultural and thermal city of Merano.

The specially selected rooms offer a bit of fun, with a vintage Polaroid camera, so you can capture a picture and enter it in the "MM" draw.

Miramonti Boutique Hotel
St.Kathreinstasse
Hafling / Avelengo
Bolzano / Alto Adige 39010
Italy
www.GoUnusual.com/MiramontiBoutiqueHotel

• Breakfast provided
• Bar / Restaurant on site

HOTEL GREIF
TRADITIONAL SETTING FOR SPECIALLY COMMISSIONED ART

"Greif" is the German word for "griffin", the mythical creature with a lion's body and an eagle's wings, beak and talons. Just as the griffin combines diverse strengths, Hotel Greif offers an exclusive setting between tradition and modernity;

Thirty-three individually extraordinary rooms have been composed by owner, Franz Staffler, and Viennese architect, Boris Podrecca, each displaying a specially commissioned artwork by a different artist. All offer a feast for the senses, featuring the luxury of raw silk, silver leaf covered walls, and fine examples of antique Biedermeier furniture.

LOCATION AND ACTIVITIES

Bolzano/Bozen is often dubbed 'Gateway to the Dolomites'. The city lies in a broad valley basin at an altitude of 265 metres (870 ft), with three beautiful Alpine high plateaux of rolling hills encircling it from north-east to north-west. It is difficult to avoid Bolzano Bozen if you are coming to the Dolomites, the breathtaking mountains are classified as a Unesco World Natural Heritage site. In spring the contrast between lush Mediterranean vegetation beside the town's panoramic sun-drenched promenades and the snow-mantled Dolomites with skiing season still in full swing, is especially striking.

Hotel Greif is located in downtown Bolzano, in the pedestrian zone, only a few minutes walk from the train station, the main shopping street with its famous arcades, theatres, concert halls and museums including the one where you can see the 5000-year old Iceman Ötzi - one of the world's best-known and most important mummies in the world.

The best restaurants, like the one at the Parkhotel Laurin are also nearby. By car it's only 10 minutes from the airport and 8 from the motorway.

"Modern art displayed in a traditional setting"

Hotel Greif
Piazza Walther / Via della Rena 28
Bolzano
South Tyrol
Italy
www.GoUnusual.com/HotelGreif

• Breakfast provided
• Bar / Restaurant on site

SAN LORENZO MOUNTAIN LODGE
A UNIQUELY SATISFYING MOUNTAIN EXPERIENCE

Formerly an elegant hunting lodge and 16th-century private retreat for the local nobility, San Lorenzo Mountain Lodge offers groups a 42-acre oasis in the Dolomites. The pristine woods and meadows will enchant even the most discriminating of guests.

The building is at an altitude of 1200 meters, so winter sporting activities followed by relaxation in the spa and pool are the order of the day. In summer, the surrounding nature provides all the entertainment required. Heating is by an ecological wood chip heating system with chips from trees felled locally. The Lodge's sustainable and ecological energy concept is rounded off by the use of water from the estate's own spring.

For 25 years, the professional livelihoods of owners Giorgia and Stefano Barbini were in the world of fashion and haute couture design. Their knowledge and attention to detail is visible in every fitting, and in their efforts to satisfy the wishes of the most demanding groups.

LOCATION AND ACTIVITIES

The Lodge has all the facilities required for the most elegant house parties, special celebrations or group trips away. Inquire and you'll discover that your wishes are welcomed - discovering a hidden gem you'll want to share with friends.

The house sleeps three couples and four children comfortably, and guests rent the entire lodge for a day, a week or longer. Most guests tick the box for VIP service, which gives you access to Giorgia - who will let you in on her secrets from the kitchen, preparing wholesome, delicious, creations that won't soon be forgotten.

Don't be surprised if you find yourself craving nothing more than sitting by the fire with a good book, or out in the garden Jacuzzi pool, sipping a glass of wine.

"Promises complete relaxation!
You have been warned!"

San Lorenzo Mountain Lodge
Elle,23 San lorenzo di Sebato
Alto Adige 39030,
Italy
www.GoUnusual.com/SanLorenzoMountainLodge

• Vacation Rental
• Group bookings 4+
• Dinner provided on request

LAURIN SUITE

DESIGNER SUITE - IN THE GARDEN OF A VINEYARD

The 101st room of the historic Laurin hotel of Bolzano is a touch of 'magic in Magrè' about a half hour south of the South Tyrol capital. This single suite is in Paradeis literally, as the estate of the Laegeder winemakers is called just that, installed though a joint venture to celebrate 100 years of Laurin's history.

Your suite is a designer 'modular dwelling' situated in the English garden of the Lageder wine estate with all the amenities of a four-star hotel. The design is an inviting combination of an exclusive façade by the young South Tyrolean artist Claudia Barcheri, and of stylish interiors equipped with antique furniture from Laurin dating from 1910, lovingly selected and restored in the hotel's own joiner's workshop.

LOCATION AND ACTIVITIES

...And paradise it is... a pebble path leads through the forested park to the room structure, painted like tree bark. It opens up into an ample open space sitting room/bedroom. Wi-fi, DVD, stereo and widescreen TV, antique parquet floors, antique furnishings from the venerable Laurin, counterpointed by an übermodern bath, separate waterfall shower and deep Jacuzzi.

You will sleep like a baby thanks to a bed and pillow combination fit for royalty, enjoying the surrounding peace and tranquillity. This haven of outdoor relaxation is maintained thanks to Nick-the-gardener, an émigré from Yorkshire, who left the UK near a decade ago to tend to this little Eden.

Naturally a bottle of Laegaeder's wine is waiting for you open, and your visit will simply not be complete without a full visit to the winery – with a brisk walk on a mountain trail to clear your head!

Alois Lageder wines can be tasted at any time in the wine bar. Winery tours take place each Thursday at 2.30pm.

"A fleeting opportunity - although open in 2013, it won't be here forever..."

Laurin Suite
Winery Paradeis
Wine estate Alois Lageder
Magreid, Bolzano
Italy
www.GoUnusual.com/LaurinSuiteParadeis

• Breakfast provided
• Bar / Restaurant nearby

VIVERE
DESIGNER COMFORTS IN A RURAL SETTING

VIVERE - "to live", where Edy and Michela balance the comforts of a low ecological impact designer property with spa and gourmet experiences based around local produce, including the properties own vineyard, olive groves, wine and honey. This young couple have taken the Italian "agritourism" concept and turned it on its head.

You are surrounded by vineyards and olive groves, yet enjoy this experience in a stylish chill-oasis, rather than a rustic farm – hidden from the surroundings by an unassuming rust-distressed gate.

Developed in cooperation with "studio Architetti Associati Gianni Calzà – Emanuele Genuizzi – Giovanni Banal" from Milan, the property uses renewable geothermal, solar and photovoltaic energy. Surrounded by the vineyards of Alto Garda, individual suites have their own private gardens and access, sharing the pool and salon.

Guests spend their time in nature, receiving Spa treatments on request, while eating and drinking high quality products from the locality, as well as the family run farm which provides Estate bottled extra virgin olive oil, DOP Trentino, Merlot DOC red wine, honey and jams.

LOCATION AND ACTIVITIES

There are four suites with kitchenette and two junior suites.

Michela and Edy greet you with amiable charm so you feel instantly at home.

All suites have their own private entrance and private garden and are equipped with all modern comforts. Guests also have available, the romantic veranda overlooking the

swimming pool, where they can enjoy their breakfast or sip drinks. During cooler evenings guests often sit by the fire and listen to music in the living room, perhaps trying the excellent wine produced from Vivere's own vineyards.

"Never have your senses been so comfortably fooled into submission!"

Vivere
Via Gobbi, 30
Arco
Trento 38062
Italy
www.GoUnusual.com/Vivere

• Vacation Rental
• Group bookings 4+
• Dinner provided on request

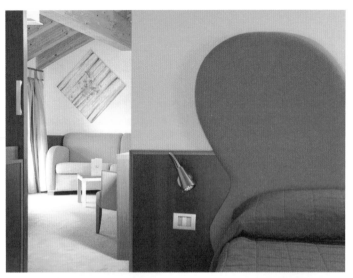

COLOR HOTEL

COLOR THEMED HOTEL NEAR SHORE OF LAKE GARDA

Colour has been proven to enhance mood sensations and the Color Hotel has used this theme to create design interiors, rooms and suites in rainbow hues for their guests.

Taking notes from chromotherapy, areas have been furnished with designer touches and Italian crafted local materials to create a get-away-from-it-all retreat, just 5 minutes from the centre of Bardolino on Lake Garda. The colour theme carries over to the rooms: Blue to favour sleep, Yellow rooms bring joy and happiness, Green areas are restful, Orange rooms are stimulating and Red, the colour of passion and romance, provides vitality. Suites overlooking the garden and pools and offer round beds and Jacuzzi tubs, some on the balcony.

The lush gardens offer a tropical atmosphere, immersed in green. Lounge areas feature fountains, original sculptures, Zen garden and a chill-out lounge. Color Hotel's H2O design is their interpretation of water as an integral element in the creation of different atmospheres within the resort: 4 separate pools and many fountains: Water, the giver of life adds vibrancy throughout.

An outstanding element is the colourful staff, from their uniforms to their sunny dispositions. Color is a delight for the eye and the palate. A meal in La Veranda restaurant is worthy of the 3 forks that Michelin have awarded it. The Italian/Dutch owners travel the world in search of the new and unusual and each visit reveals a new surprise.. the rooms with framed paintings on the ceiling, or the serene hammock lounge area.

The hotel website offers a free, fun colour profile, revealing your personality traits based on your preferences, with often surprising results.

LOCATION AND ACTIVITIES

The hotel is only a 5 minute walk from the picturesque town of Bardolino, in the south-east part of the Lake Garda, along the olive-trees seaside, 100 mts from the lake-side. The Color Hotel is in a green area of 12,000 square mts. 9 km away from Gardaland, 5 km from Canewaworld, 29 km from Verona , 32 km from the Verona Fair Center, 110 km from the romantic Venice, 130 km from Milano.

"Bright and colourful to revive the senses"

Color Hotel
Via S. Cristina, 5
Bardolino
Lake Garda
Italy
www.GoUnusual.com/ColorHotel

- Breakfast provided
- Bar / Restaurant on site

HOTEL PARCHI DEL GARDA
ANIMATRONIC THEME ROOMS

Italy's first 4D Avatar Hotel features four 'animatronic' theme rooms with amazing Hollywood style special effects to fascinate children. With 233 rooms spread out across five pavilions, facilties include a heated outdoor pool.

LOCATION AND ACTIVITIES

Just 10 minutes from Lake Garda's most famous theme park Gardaland™ the 4 theme rooms are:

Aki's cave: enter the hotel mascot's cave together with your children, where you can interact with the characters through a special keyboard.

"Theme park excitement in your room"

The Pirates Galleon room: themed as a merchant ship, it uses artificial intelligence robots to interact with guests.

The Parco Giardino Sigurtà room: a room set in nature, with green meadows, flowers blooming and tree trunks.

Natura Viva room: to live the experience of a photographic African Safari, with a very peculiar setting: a bed built on a tree dominates the scene and guests can look for the animals hidden among the trees using special software.

Hotel Parchi del Garda
Via Brusa
Pacengo di Lazise
Lake Garda 37017
Italy
www.GoUnusual.com/HotelParchidelGarda

• Breakfast provided
• Bar / Restaurant on site

JH DUNANT HOTEL
RED CROSS FOUNDER'S STORY TOLD THROUGH A HOTEL

This design-led hotel pays tribute to Jean Henri Dunant, founder of the Red Cross, the volunteer humanitarian organization conceived in Castiglione delle Stiviere.

Courageously decorated rooms highlight three aspects of the life of Dunant; Youth, Struggling economic enterprises, and finally, the Humanitarian legacy.

This isn't some stuffy museum – it positively exudes a fresh vibrant edge. Of particular interest perhaps, is the design trail, showcasing designer chairs in different rooms and public areas.

Owner Eugenio Gallina entrusted designer Ermanno Preti to create a hotel that is part museum/part installation. The concept is a hotel with zero stars - a place that cannot be defined in the traditional way but seeks judgement by the guests themselves.

Each guest room is rich in symbolism. A giant serpent is kept at bay in the courtyard; breakfast is taken at a communal spiral table, inducing guest interaction. The furnishings were deliberately upturned, sawed in half and de-conceptualized to further enhance the dreamlike atmosphere.

Design Treasure Tour:

The hotel has collected a series of globally recognised designer chairs and seats. Do not be surprised if you find a Saariner or Eams chair in your room. These pieces, which are all original, are part of an educational route, and the hotel wants guests to embark on it. Take a seat, be enriched and moved by great design.

LOCATION AND ACTIVITIES

Located in the countryside between Mantova, Verona and Lake Garda. Nearby Verona provides fantastic architecture and fascinating boutique shopping, while Lake Garda provides cafes and lakeside restaurants as well as water bourne amusement - boat rides etc.

Venice is an easy train ride away - the perfect way to visit.

"History lesson and design adventure!"

JH DUNANT Hotel
Via Donatori di Sangue 2
Castiglione delle Stiviere
Lombardia 46043
Italy
www.GoUnusual.com/DunantHotel

• Breakfast provided
• Bar / Restaurant on site

LOCANDA ROSA ROSAE
ANCIENT CONVERTED MILL NEAR TREVISO

Betty and Silvio discovered this run down mill dating from 1570 and soon fell in love with it.

Even if it was simply a ruin, it held a magic energy and unique soul. They immediately realised that it had to be saved and most of all - it had to be brought back to its ancient beauty and charm.

For Silvio, the creative architect, four years of hard sacrifice, work and research of the most stimulating and exciting kind. For Betty, blending the needs of family and guests, to comforts of the new, with the tradition and authenticity of the past.

You'll find an extraordinary sense of beauty, harmony and originality. Spaces designed in veiled lights, natural materials and objects. An atmosphere of family and peace, essential and soft.

LOCATION AND ACTIVITIES

Silvio and Betty restored everything, keeping well in mind the mill's history and austere character of the building. Using old and recycled materials, they left walls bare to the brick, and preserved the floor and the beams untreated. While the interior decoration is sparse and minimal, it has a strong, solid character, especially in the evening when lit by candles.

Without doubt you'll recognise the virtues of a simpler, more relaxed pace and find peace here.

Wander through the ancient and lush Venetian countryside, stop here at San Bartolomeo. Behind you the blurred Trevisan landscape and the whole world of Venice in front of you. In the morning discover ancient villages and grand cities, through gentle hills and virtuous vineyards.

"This is the Bed & Breakfast you'll want to tell your best friends about"

Locanda Rosa Rosae
Via Molino, 1
31030 Breda di Piave
Treviso TV
Italy
www.GoUnusual.com/LocandaRosaRosae

• Bed & Breakfast
• Dinner by arrangement (recommended)

GLAMPING CANONICI DI SAN MARCO
AMAZING GLAMPING TENTS NEAR VENICE

Furnished in a luxurious, refined yet unconventional style using ornaments and furniture collected by owners Federico and Emanuela during their travels in far-away lands, each Lodge can sleep between 2 and 5/6 guests.

"For those looking for a nature holiday without giving up comfort and refined luxury, close enough to reach Venice in less than 30 minutes, without using the car"

LOCATION AND ACTIVITIES

By Train: The nearest station is Mirano on the Venice/Padua line.

When you exit the train, walk to the end of the road, cross the intersection onto the left bank of the River Taglio (near the church). After 400 meters you'll see 'Via Canonici" on the left. The Glamping is a further 50 meters along on the left.

Set in enthralling countryside, with native trees and stupendous flower displays, you will feel immersed in nature without giving up modern comforts. The Lodges, created on a raised wooden floor, are a natural refuge after a day packed with adventure in Venice or the nearby cities of Padua and Treviso. They are an ideal base for a cultural, social, gastronomic or sporting stay, allowing you to rediscover the secret harmony that only contact with nature can generate.

Glamping Canonici San Marco
Via Canonici N. 4
Mirano, Venezia 30035
Italy
www.GoUnusual.com/GlampingCanoniciSanMarco

"Life is short. Eat the dessert first"

Ansil Baugh Blass

RISERVA 15 ANNI. IMPECCABILMENTE NARDINI.

B.^{lo} NARDINI

DISTILLERIA A VAPORE

BASSANO

— al PONTE dal 1779 —

PALAZZO BARBARIGO SUL CANAL GRANDE
ART DECO INFLUENCED DESIGN IN THIS PALATIAL VENICE HOTEL

Hotel Palazzo Barbarigo overlooking Grand Canal is an exclusive waterside hotel, next door to the famous Palazzo Pisani-Moretta, close to the Ponte di Rialto and just a 20 minute stroll from Piazza San Marco.

Built in 1569, the hotel is a fantastic example of contemporary architecture and design, updated in an Art Deco style with the latest modern facilities. Guest rooms overlook the Grand Canal or Rio di San Polo and the property represents an ideal venue for those seeking romantic seclusion.

Inside, guests encounter more surprises: a chaise longue, loveseats facing each other, a glass bar back-painted black with long, lithe legs, a headboard covered in a gauze bearing the traditional Fortuny Venetian design. The same design is silk-screened in black to frame the bathroom mirrors that feature a built-in 9-inch touch screen TV that transmits the shows being watched in the bedroom. Bathroom design has been carefully thought out to include a spacious shower with illuminated showerhead, instead of a bath tub and Corian sinks set in a silhouette vanity unit.

Palazzo Barbarigo offers 12 rooms and 6 Junior Suites, spread over two floors, overlooking the Grand Canal or the Rio San Polo. The spacious rooms are decorated and furnished in an Art Déco style, interpreting the spirit of the city and fitting perfectly with the hotel's location.

The entire palace, with its unique characteristics, is available for rent to celebrate weddings, anniversaries and special occasions for those who know how to celebrate in style.

LOCATION AND ACTIVITIES

UHOTW recommend reaching the hotel by Vaparetto or Water Taxi directly from Marco Polo airport wet basin to the hotel entrance hall. The hotel can reserve a transfer that includes a shuttle from the arrivals terminal to the wet basin, and then the motorboat to the hotel (30 min.)

"Arrive by boat to private dock on the Grand Canal"

Palazzo Barbarigo Sul Canal Grande
San Polo 2765
30125 Venice
Veneto
Italy
www.GoUnusual.com/PalazzoBarbarigo

- Breakfast provided
- Restaurants nearby

METROPOLE HOTEL
ANTIQUE COLLECTABLES IN EVERY ROOM

The Metropole once hosted the creative talents of a generation, musicians, novelists and poets, Marcel Proust, Thomas Mann, and Sigmund Freud. Now again, famous celebrities from the world of music, art and fashion have chosen the Metropole as their Venetian residence to enjoy the refined atmosphere as a discreet, quiet oasis, far from the rush and excitement of Venice, a stone's throw from Piazza S.Marco and the Art Biennale, overlooking the Island of S.Giorgio.

Details in rooms and corridors tell stories of far away lands and eclectic collections. Public galleries have glass cases filled with a veritable museum of antiques…19th century evening bags, visiting-card cases, corkscrews and nut crackers. Upstairs a splendid and unique collection of more than 100 fans from different ages.

Everywhere you look the love, passion and creativity in the family represented by Gloria Beggiato, that owns and runs the Metropole, shines through. This personal interest is what makes the Metropole so charming, as it refuses to be categorised into a specific style.

Antique furniture of the 18th century blends perfectly with that of the Orient and the Art Deco Period. Precious fabrics, fine silks and velvets in the Venetian tradition decorate rooms, and public areas.

On the ground floor, the Morocco themed Oriental Bar shares the aroma of different spices and herbs to celebrate the Tea ceremony, where from October to March you can stop and sample a ritual brew. In summer, relax in the charming Citrus Garden among the perfume of jasmines and the soft candle light.

LOCATION AND ACTIVITIES

There are 67 rooms and suites and every one is decorated in a different style. Some of the rooms have private terraces offering spectacular sunsets over the lagoon. Even the smallest junior suites have framed antiques -paintings, prints and fantastic fans from the owners private collection.

Venice has no shortage of fantastic dining experiences, and the Metropole is the venue for an original concept, the Tra'Contemporary Cuisine, where dishes of Italian regions are offered either in traditional or contemporary ways.

"An element of mystery with an oriental elegance"

Metropole Hotel
Riva Schiavoni 4149
30122 Venice
Veneto
Italy
www.GoUnusual.com/HotelMetropole

- Breakfast provided also in the garden
- Bar / Amazing restaurant on site
- Exclusive Suite Damasco with stunning Hamam

377

CA MARIA ADELE

THEMED SUITES INCLUDE THE DOGE OF VENICE SUITE

Housed within the walls of a 15th Century Palazzo, Ca Maria Adele is located in a tranquil corner of Venice's well heeled and arty Dorsoduro district. This small and intimate property overlooks the Canale and majestic Church Della Salute, and offers a majestic blend of East and West, Baroque and minimalism.

The themed rooms have been inspired by the history of Venice. Some deserve special mention:

The Doge's Room: A rich red brocade covers the walls of this room, ideally conceived to host the highest authority in the Venetian Republic. The luxury of the materials, the glimmering colours of the imposing chandelier, the gilt mirrors - will make you feel the master of the town for your stay. When you leave, only the Doge's palace itself will make you feel at home!

The Moorish Room: Venice has an exciting history of interaction with the populations it wanted to conquer (and conquer it). In the fight for domination of distant lands during the crusades, the Republic of Venice was protagonist of some of the most thrilling and fascinating pages of history. Voiceless witness of past times, the Moors are there to offer you still unknown stories of the glory of an enchanted town.

The Oriental Room: Gold and Blue symbolise Venice and it's dominion over the sea. From the canals of the lagoon, long routes bring mysterious and legendary countries - signs of the courage of the adventurous people who first united Europe with the Far East. If you yearn for the days of Marco Polo and the charm of the ancient silk road, then this room is designed for you.

LOCATION AND ACTIVITIES

The property is in the Dorsoduro district of Venice, which is known as the contemporary art neighbourhood, due to the presence of the Peggy Guggenheim Museum, the Francois Pinault Collection located in Punta della Dogana and the dynamic museum dedicated to Emilio Vedova, hosted in the Magazzini del Sale. Dorsoduro includes the Zattere and Chiesa della Salute area, which has always been regarded as one of the most exclusive districts of Venice, rich in major modern residential architectural buildings.

Everything is at less than 3 minutes' walk from Ca Maria Adele.

"If you're staying in Venice - stay here... but beware...you won't want to leave!"

Ca Maria Adele
Dorsoduro 111
Venice 30123
Italy
www.GoUnusual.com/CaMariaAdele

- Breakfast provided
- Restaurants nearby

TORRE PRENDIPARTE
TOWER IN CITY CENTER

Matteo Giovanardi has turned his former home—the second-highest of Bologna's famous medieval towers—into a one-bedroom romantic hideaway.

Following extensive restoration, all 12 floors of this 12th century tower, standing 65 metres high are accessible, including a roof terrace offering breathtaking views across the Old Town. Even the original wall graffiti of the prison cells at the foot of the tower has been preserved!

Much in demand, (from locals as well as visitors), for surprise birthday and anniversary treats - book early for favourite dates!

Although the restored staircases are steep, a handrail guides you and nothing more than sure footing is required to reach the top.

The main living and sleeping area, lounge etc. are housed on the second and third floors, in an elegant old-world space with vaulted ceilings, furnished with family heirlooms. Above this is a kitchen, where guests fix themselves a self-service breakfast, and a dining room where candlelit dinners can be arranged—accompanied, should you so desire, by a string quartet or medieval-style minstrels.

"A cosy tower for 2"

LOCATION AND ACTIVITIES

You are at the very heart of Bologna old town, with cheerful, busy streets and the hustle and bustle of this major regional hub. Take the time however, to check out the tiny streets surrounding the tower as they are filled with shops and small treasures of tradition.

Torre Prendiparte
Via Sant'Alò, 7
Bologna
40126
Italy
www.GoUnusual.com/TorrePrendiparte

- Breakfast provided
- Deluxe dinner by arrangement
- Restaurants nearby

SIENA HOUSE

OUTSTANDING INTERIOR DESIGN IN TRADITIONAL HILLTOP VILLA

An unusual stone villa dating from around 1760, in a commanding position within a protected area of outstanding natural beauty. With a large pool set away from the house, and huge vaulted lounge for guests, the fully fenced and gated property is all about comfort and privacy. Unusual in having many large windows- perhaps something to do with the super views! Bright,spacious and fully equipped for entertainment and comfort, rain or shine.

Four luxuriously appointed double bedrooms with flat TV screens, international satellite boxes & DVD players. All of the rooms have "Frette" linens, towels, bathrobes and duvets, feather pillows and orthopaedic sprung mattresses. Sanitary ware is by Phillip Starck, basins in travertine marble. Showers are open sided with non-slip sandblasted stone, with large rain shower heads.

Two of the rooms can be interconnected for family use. All rooms lead into a vast, open space, tower room where breakfast can be taken in case of cooler weather or on the terrace in case of fine weather. Bedrooms are air conditioned for the hottest days and underfloor heated for the coldest. Book breakfast in bed or join the other guests on the lawn. Raw juices, jam and home made yoghurt, with bread, muffins and cakes baked daily.

LOCATION AND ACTIVITIES

Between Rome and Florence, in the Province of Siena, the house is located within the noble Tenuta La Fratta estate. Stroll between olive and vine, forest and farmland.

Visit the world renowned wine making towns of Montepulciano (20min) and Montalcino (35min). The ancient Papal summer retreat of Pienza (20min) has beautiful architecture and astounding views of the Valley of Orcia nearby. Siena (30min) is also the location of the world famous bi-annual bare back horse race "Il Palio".

"Quality fittings, intelligent design - great vision... and a fantastic location!"

Siena House
Podere San Carlo
Localita Pietrabianca 140
Torrita di Siena
Italy
www.GoUnusual.com/SienaHouse

• Bed & Breakfast
• Two night minimum stay

FOLLONICO 4-SUITE B&B

"THE ROAD NOT TAKEN BY MOST" IN TUSCANY

Follonico invite you to experience four different environments in which to enjoy the four seasons of Tuscany. Take pleasure from the taste, the smell and, not least, the colours that characterise the passage of time.

Owners Fabio and Suzanne have brought the efficiency and comfort of modern technology to this centuries-old farmhouse, and each suite is equipped with wifi, temperature control for any season and a "raindance" shower. Each bed has a spring-independent mattress and there is a selection of pillows of different firmness and height to soothe you to sleep. This is only the beginning - there is much more that the team will invite you to discover for yourself.

Follonico's goal is not to be a hotel, a Relais in Tuscany, or a GuestHouse Bed and Breakfast (...and you'll find breakfast is probably closer to a brunch!). It is difficult to define what makes Follonico so special - beyond the meaning of individual words, they want to make you feel at home. The friendliness is familiar, but with the professionalism that accompanies early experiences from 2001 onwards. You'll be welcomed you with a smile that has always characterised Follonico and earned them the loyalty of guests from all over the world.

LOCATION AND ACTIVITIES

Located about 5 km from Montepulciano, of world renown for its Renaissance architecture and the famous Vino Nobile (the first Italian wine to carry the DOCG label). Nearby, the town of Montefollonico is a jewel of medieval origins, even more precious in that it has yet to be

'discovered' by the tourist crowds.

The main tourist areas within the province of Siena are reachable within 30-45 minutes and Follonico is 6km from Montefollonico, where you can find most of the services (restaurants, shops and markets) you will require.

Scenic walking tracks are close to the farm and you will find safe, paved roads throughout the surrounding countryside with an almost complete absence of traffic.

"Modern facilities in a traditional setting"

Follonico
Loc. Casale, 2
Montefollonico (SI)
Toscana
Italy
www.GoUnusual.com/Follonico

• Breakfast provided

CASTELLO DI PETROIA
11TH CENTURY TOWER AND CASTLE

On a hilltop, some 1200m from the main road to Perugia, this medieval castle complex sits surrounded by ancient woodlands. The birthplace of renaissance hero Federico da Montefeltro, Duke of Urbino in 1422, the entire complex was restored between 1982 and 1990, carefully preserving the authentic structure of the Castle.

The Castle is composed of three buildings: the "Castellare Maggiore" (the main part), the "Castellare Minore" (the smaller part) and the "Mastio", the building that surrounds the ancient Tower of the Castle .The 11 guestrooms are all in these three buildings.

opportunity to totally immerse themselves in the atmosphere of the Middle Ages in an unforgettable location.

LOCATION AND ACTIVITIES

The hilltop location of the castle sits on a tree-lined summit overlooking the Chiascio valley, which offers a picturesque landscape. More a home than a hotel, guests at Castello di Petroia are welcomed as family.

"A jewel from the past with luxuries of the present"

Spacious and comfortable, the bedrooms combine a sense of history and by-gone grandeur with luxurious comfort and modern conveniences. There is even an authentic 1000 year old tower converted into a 3 storey self-contained apartment. While the Tower does not offer the same level of comfort as the other rooms in the castle complex, it gives its guests the

Castello di Petroia
Località Petroia
Gubbio, Nr Perugia
Umbria 06024
Italy
www.GoUnusual.com/CastellodiPetroia

• Breakfast provided
• Bar / Restaurant on site

RISERVA PRIVATA SAN SETTIMIO
ANCIENT FARMS CONVERTED INTO SPA AND NATURE RESORT

Riserva Privata San Settimio's story began from Italo Bartoletti's love of his native land, which inspired him to set up a farm and personal country house in the 50s. With architect Ico Parisi - they started a project in the mid 70s to create a shared community village where different forms of art could be integrated. A workshop of the impossible, where craftsmen and artisans could pass on their experience to young students.

Restoring ancient farmhouse villas to create a mix of apartments, house rentals and B&B's, this idyllic rural enclave centres on an organic restaurant, spa and pool.

Villas and Apartments are offered on both a hotel and weekly rental basis, equipped with full kitchen facilities for groups wishing to enjoy the natural surroundings of the private reserve. All rooms are furnished in an elegant country style with traditional features retained. They are equipped with refrigerator, TV, hair dryer, air conditioning and heating.

Guests will find a welcome package to get them started in the kitchen including two bottles of local wine, local olive oil from the reserve, salt, sugar and specially selected tomato sauce and spaghetti.

Nearby the "Il Padiglione" restaurant combines careful service and the local ingredients from the Marche region, for hotel guests to savour for breakfast, lunch and dinner.

LOCATION AND ACTIVITIES

The Marches region includes a protected National park, as well as numerous castles and villages of historical interest.

From off-road driving, to spa treatments and pool facilities, a huge variety of interests are catered as you combine rustic charm and local ingredients with well designed facilities.

The luxurious Wellness Centre with specialized staff is at guest disposal to advise you in choosing specialized treatments and programs; Sauna, Turkish bath, Solarium, Hydromassage, Jacuzzi, Relaxation Zone and Gym.

"Nature and it's larder feel fantastic and taste great!"

Riserva Privata San Settimio
Palazzo di Arcevia
Arcevia, Ancona 60011
Italy
www.GoUnusual.com/RiservaPrivataSanSettimio

RETROME ROME
DOLCE VITA STYLE

Step back to the Dolce Vita era in this centrally located boutique B&B with original retro fittings from the 1950's & 60's.

Offering nine vintage styled and comfortable guest rooms, each with its own private bathroom, RetRome Colosseum Garden is well appointed with modern 32 inch LCD TV, DVD, WiFi internet and air-conditioning, installed without detracting from the funky vintage design. Great Italian materials and retro design with vintage originals.

A light breakfast is served at nearby café which offers impressive Colosseum views from the terrace. This arrangement allows guests to have an early or a late breakfast according to their preference.

LOCATION AND ACTIVITIES

The Colosseum Garden B&B is located 250 meters from the Colosseum in the charming "Celio" area in the center of Rome. It promises a relaxed, authentic Roman experience. All main sights of Rome including the Roman Forum, Piazza Navona, the Pantheon, Trevi Fountain, Spanish Steps are within easy walking distance.

A metro stop, tram stop and many bus lines are within 5 minutes walk of the property.

"Every room an elegant creation by itself"

Retrome Rome
Via Marco Aurelio 47
Rome 00186
Italy
www.GoUnusual.com/Retrome-Roma

SEXTANTIO
CAVE LIVING TO LUXURY STANDARDS

Restored from the abandoned and decaying ancient caves in the Basilicata village of Matera in Southern Italy, Sextantio Le Grotte della Civita offers guests the opportunity to re-evaluate their interpretation of authenticity. Daniele Kihlgren, the Swedish-Italian entrepreneur, hotelier and philanthropist, spearheaded the campaign to resuscitate the caves, breathing new life into them while honouring and highlighting the lives previously spent dwelling in their depths.

There are 18 rooms, divided into three standard rooms, nine superior rooms and six suites. As they are all caves, dimensions aren't uniform and all are different, some with 160m^2 of floorspace, others with ceilings over 6m high. Standard rooms are slightly smaller than superior rooms and all have double beds and a shower or bath. Suites are vast with vaulted ceilings, windows looking out on to the valley and its prehistoric landscape, plus kingsize beds, baths and showers. Suite 13 is a particular gem, part of a deconsecrated church with angel-shaped indents in the walls, flooded with natural light from a balcony overlooking the dramatic valley beyond.

In order to provide its guests with proper standards of luxury, the site was meticulously taken apart, entirely wired and piped and finally reassembled with each stone replaced in its original location. WOW!

LOCATION AND ACTIVITIES

Situated in the proverbial arch of the Italian boot, Matera is not a village widely known by foreigners as it has been historically impoverished and therefore entirely localised. The importance of maintaining the traditional local aesthetic and preserving the existing architecture is thus intensified in this UNESCO World Heritage Site. Matera's alleys and cave churches have even been used as a setting for Jerusalem in several films.

"An unparalleled marvel of beauty providing a truly once in a lifetime experience"

Sextantio Le Grotte della Civita
Via Civita 28, Matera
Basilicata 75100
Italy
www.GoUnusual.com/SextantioLeGrottedellaCivita

MASSERIA MONTENAPOLEONE

FORTIFIED 16TH CENTURY FARM WITH LOCAL PRODUCE DELICACIES!

As the gates of this fortified farm close behind you, you are wrapped in the beauty of nature, which invites you towards the entrance. Oleander bushes, bougainvillea and olive trees line your path. Bales of hay and an old well - still full of water, are the first whispers of the activity which will be part of your life during your stay. With "Rustic chic", re-utilising artefacts and farm instruments of long ago, the Masseria has created a warm yet stylish ambiance.

The Masseria, was refurbished and renovated not to stand out - but rather to be part of the nature around it. Some of the rooms are the original caves and dwellings of the first settlers in the area hundreds of years ago. Each room, corner and private area has been redesigned or embellished to encompass the natural beauty which it already possesses.

When you open the door of one of the suites, you are carried away to a world of serenity and unique rustic beauty. Each suite has been designed differently with revived artifacts, which are both a journey into imagination, and a memory of a time gone.

LOCATION AND ACTIVITIES

The seaside is just 5 minutes down the road from the Masseria with an abundance of relaxing and reclining choices. When driving, the Masseria Montenapoleone offers a perfect base from which to visit the main places and sites in the heart of Puglia.

Perhaps the elegant Martina Franca with its noble "old city" surrounded by stone walls with prominent Baroque gates

to the city takes your fancy, or maybe Fasano, immersed in the land of the millinery olive trees and one of the biggest Zoo Safaris in Europe. There are lots of sights to see and places to visit. We also recommend too taking the time to visit Polignano a Mare - an ancient fisherman village perched on the cliffs of the Adriatic coast.

"A sense of nostalgia transports you to a simpler time - yet you're surrounded by all modern amenities required"

Masseria Montenapoleone
C.da BICOCCA (Via delle Croci) n.8
Pezze di Greco
Puglia 72010
Italy
www.GoUnusual.com/MasseriaMontenapoleone

- Breakfast provided
- Restaurants nearby

395

MASSERIA CERVAROLO
RESTORED TRULLI DWELLINGS

This splendid Masseria (manor farm) dates from the 16th century and creates a warm sensation of peace. It is based around six ancient Trulli - which are conical stone dwellings, built without cement or mortar - so that they could be taken down should conditions require. They were the original DIY properties of their time and have been lovingly restored and connected to the main building to provide three of the 17 bedrooms.

The main property was once a working farm - presided over by noble families. Brought back to its original splendour, it is furnished with lovingly restored antiques and original fabrics.

As was the tradition for many Masseria, which were important places of safety for the poor workers in times of trouble, it gained a religious role, housing an 18th century chapel completely frescoed and dedicated to the Virgin Mary. Now restored, it adds to the charm of the property.

LOCATION AND ACTIVITIES

The property is located between the airports of Bari (50mins) and Brindisi (30mins) where you can easily rent a car. You're based in La Vallee D'Itria - the very heart of Puglia. With the beaches of the Adriatic 12km away and two large nature reserves close by (Fiume Morelli - 15mins, Torre Guaceto - 25mins), there is plenty of opportunity for walking or resting on the beach, cooled by sea breezes.

Guests sleep in a welcoming embrace where all the senses are stimulated: the sight of the white stone contrasting with the cobalt-blue sky; the intense aroma of the Mediterranean terrain that harkens back centuries, the comforting sounds of nature; the textured bark of a centennial olive tree; the taste of fresh, local cuisine.

You are surrounded by shady terraces of local vegetation and a magnificent pool faced with sandstone, the water reflecting varying shades of blue. Here you'll find a myriad of fragrances and colours, set in a land rich in folklore and tradition, and most importantly will find that the typical Puglian warmth of the host family that will capture your heart.

"A Magical Place - as indeed is Puglia: a thousand years of history, art, culture"

Masseria Cervarolo
C.da Cervarolo snc
Ostuni 72017
Puglia
Italy
www.GoUnusual.com/MasseriaCervarolo

- Breakfast provided
- Restaurants nearby

ABALI GRAN SULTANATO
THE EMBASSY TO MYTHICAL LANDS...

The Grand Sultanate of Abalì is a place where you can find five star luxury together with eclectic elegance and the friendliness of a B&B. However, it is the distinctive colours and decorations that make each room unique and unforgettable. From bright pink and lurid yellow, to rich reds, everyone will have a favourite. Perhaps a round bed, in green and purple or turquoise, - or a red tango design with king size bed. Maybe the Sultan's suite with a four poster bed and a jacuzzi in the room takes your fancy?

This is no ordinary B&B and Vito, the Grand Sultan of Abali is no ordinary host.

There are three classes of room – the Standard (double), Tango Suite and most luxurious of all, Sultan Suite. Every room has a private bathroom, air conditioning, TV and wi-fi, polished cotton sheets and soft towels. The Sultans suite is not surprisingly the most spacious, with frescoed walls, a canopy four poster kingsize bed and windows overlooking the town. The bathroom has a jacuzzi tub and a large shower.

Mohanaraja, Butler of the Court, will be at your service for your entire stay and invites you to join the Sultan for breakfast, which is served in the Royal Dining Room.

LOCATION AND ACTIVITIES

The Grand Sultanate of Abalì is situated in the historic centre of Palermo, on the corner of Via S. Agostino and Via Maqueda, the main axis of the city.

It is in an ideal position and minutes' walk from all the main tourist sights ... but the Sultan hopes you will take at least three hours for each and in this time lose yourselves in the beauty of the thousands of hidden corners that Palermo offers to the most attentive travellers.

For those with little time, the Central Station is five bus stops away while you can walk to Piazza Politeama in six minutes. The Cathedral and the Norman Palace can be reached on foot in 15 minutes.

"The Sultan is available to bargaining and forms of barter. A court will await your proposals"

Abali Gran Sultanato
Via S. Augustine, 5 (Corner of Via Maqueda)
Palermo
Sicily
Italy
www.GoUnusual.com/AbaliGranSultanato

- Breakfast provided
- Restaurants nearby

ADDITIONAL IN EUROPE
ANDORRA, AUSTRIA, CZECH REPUBLIC, FINLAND, FRANCE

ANDORRA
Iglu-Dorf Andorra
Grandvalira
Andorra
The Iglu-Dorf GmbH team have also built an Igloo resort in the Grandvalira at 2300m - (See the Engelberg entry for more details)
www.GoUnusual.com/iglu-dorfandorra

AUSTRIA
Rogner-Bad Blumau
Bad Blumau 100
Austria
Hundertwasser designed Spa resort with grass covered roofs and surreal rainbow façades. Some rooms are underground facing lit courtyards
www.GoUnusual.com/rogner-badblumau

CZECH REPUBLIC
Medieval Hotel Detenice
Bohemia
Czech Republic
Medieval themed hotel providing magical middle ages experiences in an authentic setting.
www.GoUnusual.com/MedievalHotelDetenice

FINLAND
Snow Hotel
Kemi
Finland
Charming child-focussed snow hotel in a city centre location
www.GoUnusual.com/SnowHotel

FRANCE
Airstream Europe
Bel Repayre, Manses
France
Airstream caravans available on a self-catering basis
www.GoUnusual.com/AirstreamEurope

Hotel Arbez
La Cure
France
Straddles the border. Breakfast in France, and sleep in Switzerland
www.GoUnusual.com/HotelArbez

Château de Bagnols
Bagnols,
France
Historic Chateau, restored to former glory
www.GoUnusual.com/ChateaudeBagnols

Le Prince Noir
les Baux de Provence
France
Carved out of mountainside rock, at the top of an old Roman fortress
www.GoUnusual.com/lePrinceNoir

Les Hautes Roches
Rochecorbon
Loire
France
Twelve rooms carved out of the limestone rockface and a gourmet restaurant
www.GoUnusual.com/LesHautesRoches

ONE by the Five
Paris
France
An exceptional and unique artistic design for a single incomparable suite
www.GoUnusual.com/ONEbytheFive

The Five Hotel
Paris
France
Funky rooms, including a double bed suspended from the ceiling
www.GoUnusual.com/TheFiveHotel

ADDITIONAL IN EUROPE

GERMANY, HUNGARY, IRELAND, ITALY, THE NETHERLANDS

GERMANY
Arte Luise Kunsthotel
Berlin
Germany
Centrally located co-operative Art gallery hotel sharing proceeds with artists
www.GoUnusual.com/ArteLuiseKunsthotel

Iglu-Dorf Zugspitze
Grainau, Zugspitze
Germany
An Igloo world with a view of four countries in a popular ski resort
www.GoUnusual.com/Iglu-DorfZugspitze

HUNGARY
Hotel Gellert
Budapest
Hungary
Preserved work of art hotel next to the river Danube
www.GoUnusual.com/HotelGellert

IRELAND
Clontarf Castle Hotel, Dublin
Ireland
12th Century Castle updated with superb 21st-century style and facilities
www.GoUnusual.com/ClontarfCastle

The Schoolhouse Hotel, Dublin
Ireland
Central Dublin school converted to a four star hotel in 1998
www.GoUnusual.com/TheSchoolhouseHotel

ITALY
vigilius mountain resort
Lana, South Tyrol
Italy
Car free mountain resort. Cable car access only.
www.GoUnusual.com/vigiliusmountainresort

ART Hotel Atelier sul Mare
Castel di Tusa, Sicily
Italy
Art Hotel in Sicily, with every room a work of art
www.GoUnusual.com/ARTHotelAteliersulMare

Franklin Feel the Sound
Rome
Italy
The music hotel in Rome!
www.GoUnusual.com/BestWesternHotelFranklinFeeltheSound

Residenza d'Arte
Torrita di Siena
Italy
14th Century history combined with contemporary art in the house and gardens just outside Siena
www.GoUnusual.com/ResidenzadArte

Sarah in Venice
Venice
Italy
Elegant yacht moored in Venice's lagoon available from B+B to weekly vacation
www.GoUnusual.com/SarahinVenice

THE NETHERLANDS
The Arena Hotel
Amsterdam
Netherlands
Designer hotel converted from former orphanage including trendy nightclub
www.GoUnusual.com/TheArenaHotel

ADDITIONAL IN EUROPE

THE NETHERLANDS, PORTUGAL, SPAIN, SWEDEN

THE NETHERLANDS continued

Hemp Hotel
Amsterdam
Netherlands
Friendly budget hotel in Amsterdam dedicated to the use of hemp. From food to fabrics, you'll find hemp in an amazing variety of useful things
www.GoUnusual.com/HempHotel

Hotel Filosoof
Amsterdam
Netherlands
Amsterdam hotel themed on philosophers and their works
www.GoUnusual.com/HotelFilosoof

Kruisherenhotel Maastricht
Maastricht
Netherlands
Sleep in a 15th Century monastery, artistically converted into designer hotel
www.GoUnusual.com/KruisherenhotelMaastricht

Lifeboat Hotel - Harlingen
Harlingen
Netherlands
A Watson class lifeboat lovingly restored to luxurious standard
www.GoUnusual.com/LifeboatHotel-Harlingen

Lighthouse – Harlingen
Harlingen Harbor
Netherlands
Converted Lighthouse in Harlingen historic docks - Near the City Centre
www.GoUnusual.com/Lighthouse-Harlingen

YOTEL SCHIPHOL
Amsterdam
Netherlands
Snooze space in airport offering rooms for as little as 4hrs
www.GoUnusual.com/YOTEL

PORTUGAL

Quinta dos Moinhos de S. Filipe
Setúbal
Portugal
This converted mountain-top windmill has the best ocean views!
www.GoUnusual.com/QuintadosMoinho

Nespereira Estate Nature hides / Montes de Carvaho
Alentejo
Portugal
Cork Estate with variety of theme dwellings
www.GoUnusual.com//Keyword/NespereiraEstate

SPAIN

Cuevas Pedro Antonio de Alarcón
Guadix
Spain
Pre-historic caves, now converted to year round guest accommodation
www.GoUnusual.com/CuevasPedroAntoniodeAlarcon

Gran Hotel La Florida
Barcelona
Spain
The best views in Barcelona in this restored designer hotel
www.GoUnusual.com/GranHotelLaFlorida

Marqués de Riscal
Elciego, Álava
Spain
Stunning Frank O Gehry designed wine hotel with iconic styling
www.GoUnusual.com/MarquesdeRiscal

SWEDEN

Langholmen Hotel
Stockholm
Sweden
The old Stockholm, crown prison, converted into a hotel
www.GoUnusual.com/LangholmenHotel

ADDITIONAL IN EUROPE
SWEDEN, SWITZERLAND, TURKEY

STF Sala Silvermine
Sala
Sweden
A beautiful, rustic 20 s and 50 s style B+B in a restored mine workers rooming house
www.GoUnusual.com/SalaSilvermineUndergroundsuite

SWITZERLAND
Iglu-Dorf Davos-Klosters
Davos-Dorf
Davos
Switzerland
An Igloo world in white - see main entry for Engelberg
www.GoUnusual.com/Iglu-DorfDavos-Klosters

Iglu-Dorf Gstaad
Igloo Village Gstaad
Saanenmöser
Gstaad
Switzerland
An Igloo world in white - see main entry for Engelberg
www.GoUnusual.com/Iglu-DorfGstaad

Iglu-Dorf Zermatt
Gornergrat
Zermatt
Switzerland
An Igloo world in white - see main entry for Engelberg
www.GoUnusual.com/Iglu-DorfZermatt

Hôtel Palafitte
Neuchâtel
Switzerland
Designer property on stilts. Sleep with water underneath you
www.GoUnusual.com/HotelPalafitte

Whitepod
Montreux
Switzerland
High-tech Eco-Camp for crisp, white, snow excitement
www.GoUnusual.com/Whitepod

TURKEY
Akkoy Evleri Cave Hotel
Cappadocia
Turkey
Cave hotel and museum with centuries of family history and ownership
www.GoUnusual.com/AkkoyEvleriCaveHotel

Elkep Evi
Urgüp
Turkey
Ancient cave dwelling, now converted to hotel with en suite facilities
www.GoUnusual.com/ElkepEvi

Gamirasu Cave Hotel
Urgüp
Turkey
Restored cave hotel in Cappadocia
www.GoUnusual.com/GamirasuCaveHotel

Kadirs Yörük Top Tree Houses
Antalya
Turkey
Kadirs offers fun and friendship among the 40 tree house cottages available
www.GoUnusual.com/KadirsYorukTopTreeHouses

Hotel Mardan Palace
Antalya
Turkey
Ottoman experiential luxury, including a guest reef and aquarium
www.GoUnusual.com/MardanPalace

ADDITIONAL IN EUROPE
UNITED KINGDOM

UNITED KINGDOM
Auld Kirk Hotel
Ballater, Royal Deeside, Aberdeenshire
United Kingdom
Historic Scottish Free Church converted to a stylish restaurant with rooms
www.GoUnusual.com/AuldKirkHotel

Black Mountain Yurt,
Luxury camping with flush toilet and insulated walls
Caban Casita
Groovy cabin with dedicated dog room
Showmans Waggon
Rustic waggon, with warmth and creature comfort
Under the Thatch
Ceredigion, Wales
United Kingdom
www.GoUnusual.com/Keyword/UndertheThatch

Broomhill Art Hotel
Barnstaple,
United Kingdom
Leading art and sculpture venue, with rooms and award winning restaurant
www.GoUnusual.com/BroomhillArt

Capel Pentwyn
Penallt
United Kingdom
Converted chapel viewing Wye Valley and Forest of Dean
www.GoUnusual.com/CapelPentwyn

Captain's Club Hotel
Christchurch
United Kingdom
Chic waterside hotel with nautical style and own moorings
www.GoUnusual.com/CaptainsClubHotel

Carr Hall Castle
Halifax
West Yorkshire
United Kingdom
Norman Castle Folly in a deer park with a boutique hotel style luxury interior
www.GoUnusual.com/CarrHallCastle

Castle Cottages B&B and Treehouse
Fittleworth
United Kingdom
Treehouse, cottage and barn surrounded by ancient woodland
www.GoUnusual.com/CastleCottagesTreehouse

The Citadel
Weston-under-Redcastle
United Kingdom
Pink castle folly, built in 1820's
www.GoUnusual.com/TheCitadel

College of the Holy Spirit
Isle Of Cumbrae
United Kingdom
Britains smallest cathedral, with rooms alongside Altar
www.GoUnusual.com/CollegeoftheHolySpirit

Corsewall Lighthouse
Kirkcolm, Stranraer
Spectacular views and food in a lighthouse setting
United Kingdom
www.GoUnusual.com/CorsewallLighthouse

Cove Park
Peaton Hill, Cove, Argyll and Bute
United Kingdom
Arts and Craft retreat sleeping in converted sleeping containers
www.GoUnusual.com/CovePark

ADDITIONAL IN EUROPE
UNITED KINGDOM

UNITED KINGDOM continued
The Lime Tree
Fort William
United Kingdom
Formerly the home of a clergyman, this 19C Scottish Manse is now an art gallery that provides B&B accommodation
www.GoUnusual.com/TheLimeTree

The Old Church of Urquhart
Urquhart, Scotland
United Kingdom
Beautiful converted church in Scotland
www.GoUnusual.com/TheOldChurchofUrquhart

The Old Station
Fife, Scotland
United Kingdom
Converted railway carriage close to St Andrews for golf
www.GoUnusual.com/TheOldStation

Hotel Pelirocco
Brighton
United Kingdom
Funky themed hotel inspired by pop culture, sexy sirens and maverick musicians
www.GoUnusual.com/HotelPelirocco

Snowdonia Manor
Near Blaenau Ffestiniog, Gwynedd
United Kingdom
Historic house accessed by private platform of mountain railway
www.GoUnusual.com/SnowdoniaManor

The Summerhouse
Shrewsbury
United Kingdom
Elizabethan banqueting tower likened to fairytale castle
www.GoUnusual.com/TheSummerhouse

The Windmill B&B
Scarborough
United Kingdom
Windmill in the centre of town
www.GoUnusual.com/TheWindmillBB

West Usk Lighthouse
St Brides Wentlooge, Newport
United Kingdom
Lighthouse on River Severn estuary
www.GoUnusual.com/WestUskLighthouse

Asia
Turkey, India

Key
Entries in **Bold** typeface indicate full page entries with a photo.
Others are additional indexed entries.

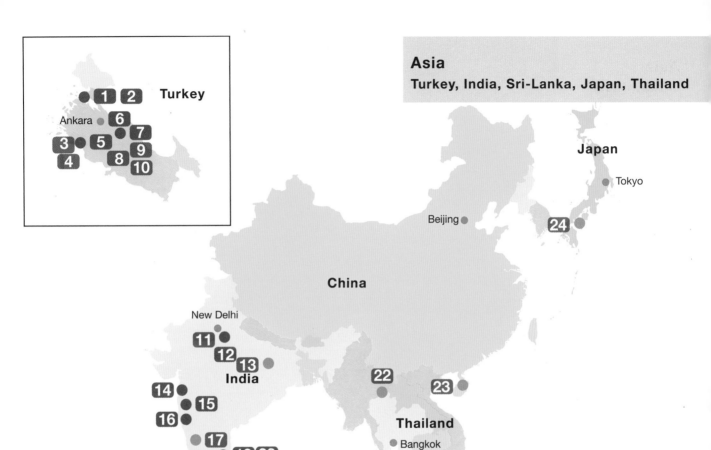

Asia
Turkey, India, Sri-Lanka, Japan, Thailand

Turkey

1
2
Ankara
6
7
3 5
4 8
9
10

Japan
Tokyo

Beijing

China

24

New Delhi
11
12
13
India

14
15
16
17
18 19 20

22

23

Thailand
Bangkok

Colombo
21

Sri Lanka

● Main photo entries
● Address entries

JAZZ HOTEL
ROOMS THEMED AROUND MUSIC LEGENDS

Jazz Hotel's 12 rooms are named after world famous jazz artists like Ella Fitzgerald and Louis Armstrong. In addition to naming rooms, each is decorated with the corresponding artist's prints and posters. The original LP is framed on every room's door - a sign of the attention to detail. Once guests open the door to their room, they are welcomed by that artist's music.

Guests can borrow jazz books, CDs and DVDs from the hotel's library and enjoy them in their rooms or the lobby. Besides using music instruments, accessories and figurines in the lobby decoration, Jazz Hotel Istanbul takes its concept to small details with music-themed clocks, ash trays, candle sticks, soaps, napkins and cookie moulds. Even the hotel staff's ties, pins and aprons are based on the theme of music. The hotel also sells music-themed gifts in the lobby.

LOCATION AND ACTIVITIES

The hotel is proud to have hosted living jazz legends like Ron Carter and Diane Schuur as guests. Jazz Hotel aims to please the jazz-enthusiast and promote jazz to the non-enthusiast, while offering a luxurious accommodation in a vibrant district.

"Rooms broadcast the corresponding artist's music"

Jazz Hotel
Bahtiyar Sokak No: 1
Nisantasi, Istanbul
Turkey
www.GoUnusual.com/JazzHotel

409

DERSAADET HOTEL
RECREATION OF 19TH CENTURY OTTOMAN MANSION

This hotel is clad in wood, replicating a late Ottoman Style homestead. Hand painted motifs in guest rooms and public spaces recreate the traditional crafts and custom furnishings that would be typical of such a dwelling. Dark wood mouldings on doors, windows and headboards; the creamy marble of the staircases, the dramatic striped marble in many of the bathrooms, and the handmade Turkish carpets in guest rooms and hallways.

In the lobby, the paintings and hand-made ceiling decoration were created by local artists inspired by Ottoman-era decoration. Along the hallways and stairways, and hanging on the guest room walls, are historic photographs of 19th-century Istanbul, when it was still known among Turks as Dersaadet, the "Gate of Felicity."

There are eight different styles of French-Ottoman style guest rooms at this carefully created and maintained 17-room wooden inn. Some deluxe rooms and junior suites have mini private hamams (Turkish bath) in the rooms, while the two Dersaadet Corner Suites, and the Sultan's Penthouse Suite have fantastic views across the sea of Marmara.

Accommodation is decorated in traditional Ottoman style, with Turkish carpets, soft wall lighting, hand-painted ceilings, and modern comforts such as individual climate control, wireless Internet, satellite TV, minibar, and direct-dial phone. The Roof Terrace, with glass-enclosed and open-air sections, serves as a lounge/café for the exclusive use of hotel guests, year-round.

A buffet breakfast is served here each morning. Throughout the day (until 23:30/11:30 pm) you may enjoy a hot or cold drink here as you watch ships steam through the Sea of Marmara and seagulls glide about the domes and minarets of the Sultanahmet (Blue) Mosque.

LOCATION AND ACTIVITIES

Dersaadet Hotel Istanbul is located in a residential neighbourhood of local families, small hotels, shops and restaurants. Few hotels are closer to the Blue Mosque than this. Though cars and buses pass on the nearby avenue, the traffic on their quiet street is more likely to be pedestrian: children playing, or on their way to school, housewives doing their shopping, or travelers exploring the area from their hotels.

Few properties are so close to the main sights of Istanbul as Dersaadet.

"Centrally located close to the main Istanbul sights, you see a slice of history from your bedroom"

Dersaadet Hotel
Kucukayasofya Cad.
Kapiagasi Sok. No:5
Istanbul
Turkey
www.GoUnusual.com/DersaadetHotel

• Breakfast provided
• Restaurants nearby

411

THE MARMARA ANTALYA
THE HOTEL SPINS AROUND TO VIEW MOUNTAINS AND SEA

Located on the famous Falez cliffs near Antalya, the world's only revolving hotel building gives guests magnificent 360° views. The complete 'Revolving Loft' annex building moves, with a full rotation of it's 24 guest bedrooms taking anywhere between 2 and 22 hours. The rotation is smooth, aided by 6 electric motors in the basement and you can go to sleep facing the sea and wake up facing the pool.

This 2750 ton building floats in a tank holding only 478 tons of water. With the 3 bottommost floors submerged, there is a lounge at the entrance and rooms on the other 3 floors. Yet somehow, the taps still work and the toilets still flush.

It is an impressive feat of engineering design.

An informal atmosphere centres around the Tuti Floor, which provides a common living space.

With glass on three sides, Tuti Floor was designed especially to offer guests the possibility for a relaxing social atmosphere in a home-from-home environment. Guests can eat while checking their e-mails, lie down on the sofas and read a book from the library, sip their drinks on the giant swing or play pool.

The Marmara Antalya offers different cuisines from round the world each night. Whether you feel like serious dining or a light snack, Tuti Restaurant, Summer Bar, Beach Bar, Revolving Lounge, food stands and beach disco give you the choice to eat and entertain whenever and whatever you like.

LOCATION AND ACTIVITIES

The Marmara Antalya is located on the eastern side of Antalya on Lara Beach, 3 kilometres from the historical centre. Guests wishing to visit the attractions will find the Aspendos Antic Theatre 35 kilometres away and the Koprulu Canyon rafting center, 90 kilometres from the hotel.

"Greet the day with an infinite Mediterranean scenery and go to sleep with a view of the pool"

The Marmara Antalya
Eski Lara Yolu. No : 136
Sirinyali Antalya
Mahallesi
Turkey
www.GoUnusual.com/TheMarmaraAntalya

• Breakfast provided
• Bar / Restaurant on site

MUSEUM HOTEL
ANCIENT ROOMS CARVED INTO MOUNTAINSIDE

Located in one of the most outstanding area of Cappadocia, famed for stunning fairy chimney landscapes, caves and caverns, the Museum Hotel is far from ordinary.

Based on a restoration of existing ruins and caves, careful consideration was given to preservation of original features by Omar Tosun - a well known collector of historic artifacts. His influence is not only found in the presentation of treasures, but in the stories and explanations of the history of the region, and the centuries old traditions of the area.

From the outset, the Museum Hotel has aimed to excel, providing extraordinary service to its 30 guest rooms. Since its opening, it has welcomed many prominent guests, keen to enjoy the blend of service, luxury and stunning location.

LOCATION AND ACTIVITIES

All rooms, the restaurant and terraces are decorated like a museum - and share grand views of the Ercives mountain, Red Valley, Avanos, Goreme and Pigeon Valley - some of the most stunning and important sights of the Cappadocia region.

Offering private wellness massage services in rooms or, during summer months, on the Massage terrace, the Museum Hotel welcomes guests who want to be pampered.

Enjoy both the cooking or perhaps even lessons by the head-chef of Lil'a Restaurant - Mustafa Buyukhan, an International and National award winner for Classic and Modern Turkish Cuisines. His efforts and those of his team

satisfy the demanding palates of many international celebrities, in a property where every guest is valued.

"Stunning landscape, excellent service and inner calm for deep relaxation"

Museum Hotel
Tekelli mah. No.1 Uchisar
Nevsehir
Cappadocia 50240
Turkey
www.GoUnusual.com/MuseumHotel

• Breakfast provided
• Bar / Restaurant on site

CAPPADOCIA CAVE RESORT & SPA
LUXURIOUS CAVE HOTEL

Need to relax? Head straight to the spa in the hotel - or take a dip in one of the pools while admiring the view. The exclusive spa area offers all kinds of treatments — everything spa fans could want.

LOCATION AND ACTIVITIES

Cappadocia is truly one of the world's wonders. Dwellings, chapels and monasteries have been hewn from the rock as far back as 4,000 B.C.

"Panoramic view of breathtaking lunar landscape"

Literally built right into a mountain, the luxury hotel Cappadocia Cave Resort & Spa in Nevsehir offers a spectacular panorama view over the dramatic jagged landscape of Cappadocia. This region in Anatolia, known for its cave structures, is a UNESCO world heritage site. But not only are the surroundings are breathtaking: this 5 star hotel does its utmost to pamper each guest from top to bottom. Well designed rooms and suites with their romantic cave atmosphere let you enjoy every modern comfort.

The combination of cave walls, fine woods and high quality natural stone is unique. Combining a restaurant, three bars, two pools, cozy cave accommodation and an exclusive, cave-built private spa, you'll make memories that will last a lifetime. Rooms are available in six categories, ranging from "Superior Room" to the "PadiShah Suite", (handicapped accessible rooms also available).

Cappadocia Cave Resort & SPA
Tekelli Mah. Goreme Cad.
Divanli Sk. No:83 Uchisar
Nevsehir, Cappadocia
Turkey
www.GoUnusual.com/CappadociaCaveResortandSPA

• Breakfast provided
• Bar / Restaurant

417

NEEMRANA FORT PALACE
RESTORED HISTORIC FORT AND PALACE

Built in 1464, Neemrana Fort Palace became the third capital of the descendants of Prithviraj Chauhan III, who had fled Delhi in 1192 after he was vanquished in battle by Muhammad Ghori. Neemrana's rulers, proud of lineage, continued to assert themselves, even under the British, as their kingdom suffered.

Eventually, Raja Rajinder Singh of Neemrana moved away to Vijay Bagh and the Fort-Palace crumbled and its ramparts began to give way. For forty years he tried to rid himself of his liability but there were no takers. Finally, in 1986, the ruins were acquired for restoration and after 5 years of work, Neemrana Fort - Palace opened its doors with the nobility of its façade raised, and the first 15 rooms available to guests.

Rooms are furnished with a mix of traditional Indian and colonial furniture. Most rooms have private balconies or terraces. With no shortage of rooms, some doubles are available at bargain prices - perfect for romance on a budget.

Neemrana Fort Palace has all the facilities of a modern 5-star resort, in a truly historic setting, allowing you to enjoy modern comforts while you relax in a reminder of a royal past.

LOCATION AND ACTIVITIES

Neemrana Fort Palace is not just a hotel. An additional wing now houses the pool and health spa, an amphitheatre, the hanging gardens with a salon, a restaurant with a roof-top garden and conference rooms and many special suites.

All efforts have been made to maintain the old charm of the property and to ensure basic comforts that have come to be associated with the changes in lifestyle since 1464 are provided. Neemrana offers a unique experience of seeing and 'living' history. Nothing about Neemrana is ordinary.

Must try: *Above the fort lies India's first "zip tour", offering a thrilling new aerial adventure, using multiple zip lines criss-crossing the valley.*

"Few places can afford guests the lifestyle of a Raja. Neemrana is one such discovery"

Neemrana Fort
Neemrana, Alwar
Rajasthan 301705
India
www.GoUnusual.com/NeemranaFortPalace

• Bed & Breakfast
• Dinner by arrangement
• Hotel bar

TREEHOUSE HIDEAWAY
TREEHOUSES NEXT TO TIGER RESERVE

Treehouse hideaway is in the heart of wild country Bandhavgarh and only 10 minutes drive from the Tala gate of the national park. Guests benefit from the incredible location, outstanding hospitality and a naturalist team. There are 5 Treehouses spread across a natural forest clearing in a dense jungle of 21 acres that merges into one of the last natural tiger reserves of the world.

It is not uncommon to spot animals from the privacy of one's balconies which overlook the tiger reserve.

Designed to provide a rustic jungle setting, retaining modern conveniences and design, the tree houses are self contained and a perfect getaway for couples keen on privacy.

The bedrooms are furnished with understated, modern accessories in natural and earth tones. All tree houses have modern attached bathrooms with 24 hour hot and cold water, a living area, mini bar, split air conditioners with power back up, mosquito netting, writing table & chair, and loungers in the balconies.

Dining takes place around a large Mahua tree, on two levels. The ground level serves as a cosy dining hall and the terrace as a bar known as the Watering Hole. The resort offers Indian, Continental and barbecue meals personalized to the requirements of the guests.

LOCATION AND ACTIVITIES

Bandhavgarh is a small National Park; compact, yet teeming with wildlife.

The density of the Tiger population is the highest known in India. The Hideaway in itself is geared up for many tour options and the on-site trained naturalist team makes it all the more interesting. Inside the park you have the option of leaving the jeep and getting on an elephant to take your chance of getting close to a tiger.

"Tiger National Park access from a Treehouse base"

TreeHouse Hideaway
Village Ketkiya
Bandhavgarh, Dist Umaria
Madhya Pradesh
India
www.GoUnusual.com/TreeHouseHideaway

• Breakfast provided
• Resort Property with packaged trips
• Open 15th Oct to 30th June

THE VERANDAH IN THE FOREST
ONE OF THE LAST BRITISH HILL STATIONS

Among paths once cleared by the British in the forests of Matheran, The Verandah in the Forest is the last British hill station. A century on, it has acquired a new identity as the place where Bombay's movers and shakers meet. Guests, from film stars to businessmen, come to spend a few quiet and peaceful days to enjoy the cooler airs as they rest in the peace and tranquility of this car-free resort.

Perched atop the Sahyadri ranges, Matheran is Asia's only pedestrian hill resort. Chug up in a toy train, trot, or arrive in a palanquin, past gigantic mansions built by the British, the Parsis, and the Bohras.

This property was originally built for other purposes. All efforts have been made to maintain the old charm of The Verandah in the Forest while ensuring the basic comforts that have come to be associated with the changes in lifestyle since the 19th century.

LOCATION AND ACTIVITIES

The parking of The Verandah in the Forest is located at the Dasturi Car Park, approximately 4.5 km away from the hotel. Cars are not allowed inside Matheran. From Dasturi one can walk, hire coolies (for your baggage), ride a horse, or take a hand pulled rickshaw to reach the property.

The journey up to Matheran takes about one and a half hours and guests are advised to reach Dasturi well before the sunset to relish the jungle and to truly enjoy their arrival at The Verandah

Matheran is encircled by red mud paths with as many as 33 look-out points that offer picturesque views! Horse riding and trekking are some of the other activities Matheran is famous for..

"Hill resort with Pedestrian access only"

The Verandah in the Forest
Barr House
Matheran, Maharashtra
India
www.GoUnusual.com/TheVerandahintheForest

• Breakfast provided
• Restaurant on site

ELSEWHERE BEACH HOUSES
TRADITIONAL GOAN – PORTUGUESE BEACH HOUSES

Four simple but charming houses sleeping 2-6 people, located on an idyllic, secluded beach in North Goa, separated from the rest of the world by a quiet salt water creek. "Elsewhere" is far from the tourist trail and likely you'll only see the footprints of fishermen and sea turtles on the miles of sandy beach.

Once a coconut plantation dating back to 1886, the location preserves the privacy and peace of guests, with the salt water of the creek keeping even the mosquitos away.

Elsewhere houses are run like a little hotel. They have housekeeping and a dining shack area where you order food from a menu and pay for what you order at the end of your stay.

LOCATION AND ACTIVITIES

Your location is one of the nicest, beaches in Goa and an outdoor shower is provided for when you return from the beach. All the 4 houses sit on the beach facing the sea. They are built in a traditional style with thick, cool, walls, shuttered windows, cool natural flooring and a lofty terracotta tiled sloping roof. The furniture is a mix of traditional and rustic. All have a delightful open sitting area to watch the sea by day and the stars by night.

Elsewhere Beach Houses are available to rent for a minimum period of one week. A Housekeeper / cleaner is included and bed linen and towels are changed regularly. Electric fans are provided in all the bedrooms and two of the houses are air conditioned.

The salt water creek is mosquito free, although electric mosquito repellent is provided in bedrooms.

The Elsewhere Beach Houses will be closed from June 1st till Sept 30th for the Monsoon season.

"Secluded access to remote, sandy beach"

Elsewhere Beach Houses
Otter Creek
Near Mandrem
Goa
India
www.GoUnusual.com/ElsewhereBeachHouses

- Vacation Rental
- 2 night min stay
- Flexible dining options

OTTER CREEK TENTS
LUXURY TENTS ON PRIVATE BEACH IN GOA

Three exclusive, comfortable tents on an idyllic, secluded beach in North Goa, separated from the rest of the world by a quiet salt water creek. A coconut plantation dating back to 1886 owned by the Sequeira family, the secret location preserves the privacy and peace of guests, with the salt water of the creek keeping even the mosquitos away.

Otter Creek Tents is run like a little hotel. They have housekeeping and a dining shack area where you order food from a menu and pay for what you order at the end of your stay. The cost of a meal per person is approximately 4 UK Pounds Sterling depending on what you order.

LOCATION AND ACTIVITIES

Each tent sleeps 2 in a four-poster double bed and has an en suite western style toilet and bathroom with running water and hot shower. Each tent also has its own sit-out and a bamboo jetty, over the creek. The tents use the dining facilities of the charming "Elsewhere" beach houses and both enjoy over a mile of pristine beach where one can still see the footprints of fishermen, and during the season, possibly the prints of sea turtles.

Each tent has a refrigerated minibar and a housekeeper is included with bed linen and towels changed regularly.

Although you're remote there is a Night and Day watchman, plus the facilities of the 'Elsewhere' beach house villas nearby.

You are within 100 meters of one of the finest beaches in all of Goa, overlooking a salt water / mosquito free creek.

For an additional fee a car and driver can be provided if you want shopping or to explore the region a little more.

"Rustic and Peaceful, perfect for enjoying the eclectic charm of Goa"

Elsewhere Property
Otter Creek Tents
Near Mandrem
Goa
India
www.GoUnusual.com/OtterCreekTents

- Vacation Rental
- 2 night min stay
- Flexible dining options

LE COLONIAL

COLONIAL HOUSE DATING BACK TO 1506

Le Colonial is probably Asia's oldest colonial house – dating back to 1506. It is reputed to have housed Vasco da Gama and, as the only grand European-style house near the new church, perhaps St.Francis. After 150 years as the Portuguese Governor's home, it was one of the rare houses not to be destroyed when the Dutch took Fort Cochin. Their Governors used it till Jan van Spall sold it to the British in 1795. They then passed it to J.Thomas, the legendary English trader of Tea.

The house is steeped in history – with black and white photographs and historic paintings adorning the walls as well as historic artifacts on display. Not only will you be treated to excellent service and quality furnishings, you'll enjoy your stay in this treasure trove of history.

Five captive centuries of history have been lovingly restored and embellished with every comfort. Art treasures from the colonial past now revive a scent of that era, making it a rather exclusive 'club' for discerning travelers.

Each room is named and styled after the people who lived or passed by or would have wished to take it over! Jan van Spall, Major Petrie, J Thomas, Vasco da Gama, Mahé de la Bourdonnais, Tipu Sultan, the Viceroy and his ADC.

LOCATION AND ACTIVITIES

Le Colonial is located in the very heart of historic Fort Cochin, next door to the Saint Francis Church. The sea shore and Chinese Fishing nets are only a couple of minutes walk away.

Restaurants, bars and coffee shops are abundant in this part of town. Stroll the back streets, visit the local art galleries, shop for jewellery, antiques or trendy clothing.

A motor-rickshaw taxi ride away is Jew-Town, with its historic synagogue and rows of antique shops.

"Living museum with treasures from bygone ages"

Le Colonial
1/315, Church Road, Vasco da Gama Square
Kochi
Kerela 682001
India
www.GoUnusual.com/LeColonial

• Bed & Breakfast
• Dinner by arrangement

THE BUNGALOW ON THE BEACH
HISTORIC BEACHFRONT PROPERTY

The restored Bungalow stands as a reminder of a Danish Governor and Admiral sent by the king of Denmark with two ships to open up the spice trade. Well received by the Nayak ruler of Tanjore and given this territory, the Danish East India Company built Dansborg Fort in 1620 to export pepper to Denmark.

Thrangambadi, 'land of the waves' in Tamil, became Tranquebar for the Danes and still shares many connections with this far away land. The oldest Lutheran church in India was built here in 1706 following the establishment of a printing press and the translation of the Bible into the local Tamil Language. The Danes remained until 1845 when the territory was sold to the British Raj, and it became the home of British Administrator of the area.

The property was sensitively restored in 2004. Each of the eight bedrooms has high ceilings and that great luxury when travelling, space. They are named after Danish ships of the period – which were themselves named after their patrons or figures from the period.

LOCATION AND ACTIVITIES

This picturesque coastal town lies 15 km south of the ancient Chola port of Pumpuhar, and 15 km north of the former French comptoir of Karikal. From 1620 to 1845 it was a Danish settlement ruled by Governors. Following it's sale in 1845 the British took over its administration until India's independence. This historic area is one of the first settlements in India by foreigners keen to open up the riches of the spice trade. There is plenty to see.

The Dansborg Archaeological Museum situated inside the fort holds a collection of curios and artefacts dating back to the Danes. It also has fossils of early centuries, coins, fish bones, Chinese porcelain and weapons. Rare paintings of Maratha kings and palm leaf manuscripts are also stored here.

The 700 year old Masilamani Nathar Temple built in 1306 by the Pandya King Maravarmam Kulasekara Pandyan is unique in its architecture. It was built combining Chinese architecture with Tamil architectural technique, possibly in an attempt to attract Chinese merchants who were visiting India. It touches the pool edge of the property and is no effort to visit.

"Grandeur and Colonial history in a beachfront location"

The Bungalow on the Beach
24 King Street
Tharangambadi, District Nagapattinam
Tamil Nadu 609313
India
www.GoUnusual.com/TheBungalowontheBeach

• Breakfast provided
• Restaurant on site

THE GATE HOUSE
TAMIL VILLA, HERITAGE RESTORED

Tharangambadi, 'dancing waves' in Tamil, was once a small village on the Coromandel coast in south-east India. In 1620, a Danish admiral, ambassador of the King of Denmark, arrived here to study pepper trade options. The Danes christened the village 'Tranquebar' and erected a distinctive Danish Fort, 'Dansborg'. In the 1690's many Danes bought houses in the area and gradually a small Danish township took shape, with a Tamil colony beyond.

The fort still stands as a protected monument and the Gate House, has been restored as an example of indigenous Tamil architecture with red tiled roofs and 6 rooms surrounding a central courtyard.

It stands next to the gateway to a world of white homes and Lutheran churches, ringed with palms and a cooling pool now laid in its court at the back. The rooms are traditional but refurbished with fine pieces of collector's art and furniture in a contemporary, uncluttered feel. Bedrooms are named after the temple cities of the region, with high ceilings keeping the rooms cool in the summer.

From doors to pillars, chairs and tables to cots and almirahs, every item is an authentic period piece. The courtyard, corridor, stairway and rooms lend a feeling of space, privacy and pampered luxury. The gentle breeze of the sea – barely a 10 minute walk away – and the intoxicating smell and sight of vintage teak wood furniture, sepia-toned photographs, paintings and artefacts, make the 'Gate House' a perfect example of conservation.

Bathrooms are of a high standard with modern facilities, but the bar and all meals are taken in the Bungalow on the Beach property, 5 minutes walk away.

LOCATION AND ACTIVITIES

Today you can drive in through a beautiful gate of the majestic King Street, past Lutheran churches and grand bungalows of the Danish Governor and British merchants. Gate house is situated walking distance from "Bungalow on the Beach".

"Tamil house, with period fittings and pool!"

The Gate House
24 King Street
Tharangambadi
Tamil Nadu 609313
India
www.GoUnusual.com/TheGateHouse

• Bed & Breakfast
• Dinner by arrangement

Africa

Morocco, South Africa, Tanzania, Israel, United Arab Emirates

Key

Entries in **Bold** typeface indicate full page entries with a photo. Others are additional indexed entries.

Rabat

2 ● ● **1**
Morocco

Israel

Jerusalem
●
9

Africa
Morocco, South Africa,
Kenya, Tanzania, Israel,
United Arab Emirates

10 **11** ●

Kenya
3 ●
Nairobi ●

Tanzania
● ●
4 **5** ● Zanzibar

6 ●

South Africa

7 **8** ●
Cape Town

● Main photo entries
● Address entries

ANA YELA

"PLACE OF INSPIRATION" BUILT AROUND AN ANCIENT LOVE STORY

The name AnaYela translates as "I am Yela", which are the opening words of a hidden love letter found in a niche when building works started. The letter tells the romantic love story of a girl called Yela who once lived in this house. One of the most renowned Koranic calligrapher in Marrakech hammered the story in silver on the vast doors in chronological order through the house, like pages in a book, so each room becomes a chapter of the story. This magic love story sets the atmosphere of this Arabian Night's palace. Following the style of a traditional riad, each of the five rooms are situated around a central courtyard, with a heated swimming pool taking centre stage. The flat roof terrace offers spectacular views across the city, the surrounding desert, the palm tree oasis and the snow-capped peaks of the Atlas Mountains.

Breakfast and dinner can be served on the romantic Magic Carpet, the little tower on top of the terrace, where, in the love story, the young Yela met her husband and stole her first kiss. The outstanding service of the AnaYela team was also awarded by a special prize at the 2009 World Hotel Awards.

LOCATION AND ACTIVITIES

Set in the heart of Marrakech's Medina - the ancient, spiritual part of Marrakech, AnaYela is a perfect place for all those travelers who are looking for the key to open the door to the magic of the culture and the people of Marrakech.

Marrakech, the Djama el Fna market and the Medina are places that every adventurous person has to visit... and once you've visited once, you'll be back. Take a hamam, enjoy a guided walk by the traditional desert Blue Men.

Negotiate for spices at the market. See the sights, smells and vibrancy of this amazing destination - and practice your rusty French!

World Hotel Award winner - Unique Small Hotel

Ana Yela
28, Derb Zerwal
Marrakech
Morocco
www.GoUnusual.com/AnaYela

• Bed & Breakfast
• Dinner by arrangement

KASBAH DU TOUBKAL

BERBER RETREAT WITH THE BEST VIEWS AND HOSPITALITY

The Kasbah du Toubkal is an extraordinary venture, the product of an imaginative Berber and European partnership. There is a shared belief that the beauty of the Toubkal National Park should be accessible to all who respect it. To this end the Kasbah has been transformed using traditional methods, from the home of a Feudal Caid into an unprecedented haven; one that provides a variety of accommodation and event possibilities to meet differing requirements. The Kasbah is a welcoming environment for those seeking comfortable mountain refuge, and for those who wish for superb rooms in a stunning setting. The Kasbah du Toubkal is not a hotel in the traditional sense, it is more an extension of the hospitality that stems from the home of the Berbers who run it.

Run as a partnership with the local Berber community, a five per cent levy is included in guest accommodation bills, funnelled back to the villagers for community projects etc.

The Kasbah is as much a berber hospitality centre as a traditional hotel, where the genuine friendliness, warmth and hospitality are exceptional.

The Kasbah offers a wide range of accommodation from a spectacular Garden Suite (125 sq m) with 12 m of glass wall looking up to Jbel Toubkal, through Deluxe and Standard en suite rooms to Berber Salons with gallery sleeping areas for families and groups.

LOCATION AND ACTIVITIES

The Kasbah du Toubkal is 60km from Marrakech, at the foot of Jbel Toubkal - the highest peak in N.Africa.

Talk to the Kasbah team about your transport needs. They can also organise transfers between Marrakech and Imlil.

At 1800 metres above sea level, The Kasbah unobtrusively looks out over three major valleys carved out of majestic rocky mountains rising to over 4000 metres.

"Become an honorary berber!"

Kasbah du Toubkal
Toubkal National Park
Jbel Toubkal
Morocco
www.GoUnusual.com/KasbahduToubkal

- Bed & Breakfast available
- Groups & Packaged trips welcome
- Full board Dining available

HIPPO POINT WILDLIFE SANCTUARY
PAGODA FOLLY IN THE MIDDLE OF A WILDLIFE SANCTUARY

mahogany panelled lounge and drawing room.

Welcoming guests for an overnight stay or bespoke rental, the tower and its staff cater for guests to enjoy their day at a leisurely pace.

LOCATION AND ACTIVITIES

Guests have unrestricted access to the property and its surroundings. Fishing, water-sports and riding can be arranged, as can game drives at next door private reserves.

The estate is 80 miles (150km) from Nairobi on recently paved roads. Guests should allow at least 2 hours for road transit, or consider a private plane charter.

This delicate 115 foot (40m) Kenyan Cypress-clad pagoda offers four double rooms and a single inside the nine storey construction. Nestling within the surrounding yellow acacia 'fever' trees that surround much of Lake Naivasha, the design is completely accepted by wildlife, fooling short sighted hippopotami to think that the Tower is part and parcel of the landscape, a towering yellow acacia itself. It offers close up views of monkeys, birds, giraffe, impala, zebra and of course the hippo's that give the place its name.

Originally planned as a weekend escape for Dodo and husband Michael when visiting their 600 acre Nderit estate. The top of the tower provides a 360 degree observation lookout, while a floor below is a minaret-style meditation room, furnished with big cushions and a surround view. The middle tiers of the tower offer bedrooms with crisp linens and covered verandas. Down spiral stairs and you reach a

"Garden of Eden retreat offers a magical beauty and sense of peace and harmony to guests"

Hippo Point Private Estate & Wildlife Sanctuary
P.O. Box 1852
Naivasha,
Kenya
www.GoUnusual.com/HippoPointWildlifeSanctuary

- Packaged trips only
- 2 night min stay
- Full board dining

SHU'MATA CAMP

THE MASAI NAME FOR "HEAVEN"

Large East African tents, in true Hemingway style, form a line on a hill with magnificent views in all directions. Each tent has its own veranda so you're really at one with the amazing African vista.

Luxury tents have en-suite bathrooms, flush toilets and showers colourfully decorated with Masai Art. Hot water for the showers is prepared on an open fire and delivered to your bathroom. Each tent has its own veranda with big, gauze-covered, panoramic tent windows for up-lifting views. They overlook miles and miles of African vastness that is the private Amboseli plains, the seven sisters and Kilimanjaro.

Each guest tent is spacious and equipped with a dressing table, Hemingway style hanging cupboard, bedside tray stands and a nostalgic lockable trunk for personal belongings. They create an atmosphere of the safari life of the 1920's.

LOCATION AND ACTIVITIES

The Camp is located at the foot of Kilimanjaro, deep in Masai land, in an area known as South Amboseli. Off the beaten safari tracks, an unspoilt wilderness awaits you.

"Timeless moments that will last a lifetime."

Shu'mata camp
South Amboseli
Kilimanjaro
Tanzania
www.GoUnusual.com/Shumata

- Packaged trips preferred
- 2 night min stay
- Full board dining

443

HATARI LODGE
LUXURY BUSH HOTEL WITH FAMOUS HERITAGE

LOCATION AND ACTIVITIES

Hatari Lodge is situated at the northern edge of Arusha National Park - in the heart of Tanzania. Measuring roughly 300 square kilometres it combines within its boundaries the vast variety of many other parks in northern Tanzania.

Adjoining one of Africa's most beautiful and diverse national parks, Hatari Lodge is a luxurious, boutique hotel in the African bush. In view of Kilimanjaro, it offers breathtaking views onto the Momella meadow, rich with wildlife and filled with the vast beauty of Africa. Close encounters with wildlife on game drives, adventurous canoe trips or closely watch resident buffalo, giraffe and other animals as they come to you while you relax on the game viewing platform.

Owners Marlies and Jörg Gabriel have a background in safari hospitality. They have rebuilt the farm that 'Hatari!' film actor Hardy Krüger once called his own, offering nine lovingly decorated and comfortably furnished rooms. Decorated in a modern retro style giving tribute to the 60's and 70's, the oldest building serves as a large central living and dining room where guests will enjoy delicious cuisine.

Here you will find a cosy lounge area with an open fireplace, bar with a veranda and viewing deck, as well as a library.

"A true and original part of Africa"

Hatari Lodge
Arusha National Park
Mt Meru
PO Box 3171
Tanzania
www.GoUnusual.com/HatariLodge

- Packaged trips preferred
- 2 night min stay
- Full board dining

ADDITIONAL PROPERTIES
ASIA, ISRAEL, SOUTH AFRICA, SRI LANKA AND THAILAND

CHINA
Sanya Nanshan Treehouse Resort and Beach Club
Nanshan Resort District, Sanya
China
Tree houses with a great ocean view in a 5000 acre Buddhist Theme Park
www.GoUnusual.com/SanyaNanshanTreehouse
ResortandBeachClub

INDIA
The Manor
Friends Colony (West)
New Delhi
India
An oasis of calm in the centre of sprawling Delhi.
www.GoUnusual.com/TheManor

Safariland Treehouse Resort
Mudumalai National Park
Tamil Nadu
India
Treehouses adjoining conservation area
www.GoUnusual.com/SafarilandTreehouseResort

ISRAEL
The American Colony Hotel
Jerusalem
Israel
Former Pasha's palace that has been managed through generations as a residence of quality, bringing guests a place in the history of Jerusalem
www.GoUnusual.com/TheAmericanColony

JAPAN
Benesse House
Kagawa
Japan
A stunning museum of modern art with rooms
www.GoUnusual.com//BenesseHouse

SOUTH AFRICA
Breakwater Lodge
Cape Town
South Africa
Prison converted to student and conference accommodation
www.GoUnusual.com//BreakwaterLodge

Jambo Guest House
Cape Town
South Africa
Homely B+B with original art
www.GoUnusual.com//JamboGuestHouse

Sun City
North West Province
South Africa
Water park, Casino and Hotel complex in dramatic safari setting
www.GoUnusual.com//SunCity

SRI LANKA
Kumbuk River Resort
Buttala
Sri Lanka
Sleep inside a 40ft Elephant!
www.GoUnusual.com//KumbukRiverResort

THAILAND
Anantara Golden Triangle Resort and Spa
Chiang Saen, Chiang Rai
Thailand
Elephant rescue camp, luxurious resort and spa
www.GoUnusual.com//AnantaraGoldenTriangleResortandSpa

ADDITIONAL PROPERTIES
TURKEY AND THE MIDDLE EAST

TURKEY
Akkoy Evleri Cave Hotel
Cappadocia
Turkey
Cave hotel and museum with centuries of family history and ownership
www.GoUnusual.com/AkkoyEvleriCaveHotel

Elkep Evi
Urgüp
Turkey
Ancient cave dwelling, now converted to hotel with en suite facilities
www.GoUnusual.com/ElkepEvi

Gamirasu Cave Hotel
Urgüp
Turkey
Restored cave hotel in Cappadocia
www.GoUnusual.com/GamirasuCaveHotel

Kadirs Yörük Top Tree Houses
Antalya
Turkey
Kadirs offers fun and friendship among the 40 tree house cottages available
www.GoUnusual.com/KadirsYorukTopTreeHouses

Hotel Mardan Palace
Antalya
Turkey
Ottoman experiential luxury, including a guest reef and aquarium
www.GoUnusual.com/MardanPalace

UNITED ARAB EMIRATES
Desert Palm Resort, Dubai
UAE
Polo lawns provide an oasis of mystique touched with the Avant-garde style
www.GoUnusual.com//DesertPalmResort

Emirates Palace Hotel, Abu Dhabi
UAE
Service and luxury fit for a King and deserving of an Emperor
www.GoUnusual.com/EmiratesPalaceHotel

Australia and New Zealand

Key
Entries in **Bold** typeface indicate full page entries with a photo.
Others are additional indexed entries.

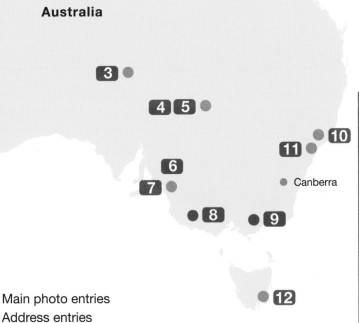

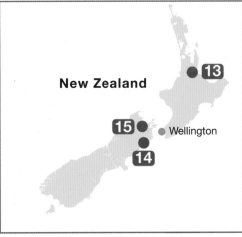

Australia and New Zealand

Australia

1

2 •

3 •

4 5 •

11 10 •

• Canberra

6

7 •

• 8

9 •

12

New Zealand

13 •

15 • • Wellington

14

● Main photo entries

● Address entries

THE OLD MOUNT GAMBIER GAOL
CONVERTED PRISON

The Old Mount Gambier Gaol was opened in 1866 and closed as a prison in 1995.

Recently refurbished, the Gaol offers unique, affordable, backpacker and boutique style accommodation in both cell and non-cell rooms to travellers of all ages.

Having travelled and worked throughout the world Managers Melissa and James have an abundance of experience in the hospitality industry and know what travellers value and need.

Guests have access to the many historic features of The Old Mount Gambier Gaol; The prison chapel, library and lounge are converted to common areas equipped with internet, colour television and sofas. The study area is the perfect place to relax, read a book, surf the net or hang out with friends and family. There are three courtyards on site available to guests for outdoor activities including live entertainment and concerts. Guests have twenty-four hour access to the communal kitchens where they can prepare a hearty meal or grab a quick snack. Food can be stored in the communal fridges and tea, coffee, sugar and milk are supplied at no extra charge.

LOCATION AND ACTIVITIES

Mount Gambier's location between Adelaide and Melbourne makes it an ideal stop over for travellers on their way through to The Great Ocean Road, Grampians and The Coonawarra Wine Region. Mount Gambier is famous for its 'Blue Lake' and is surrounded by volcanic craters, lakes, National Parks and walking tracks.

The Old Mount Gambier Gaol is located in the centre of town at 25 Margaret Street - a short walk to the main shopping precinct.

"A memorable overnight in a great location"

The Old Mount Gambier Gaol
25 Margaret Street
Mount Gambier
South Australia 5290
Australia
www.GoUnusual.com/TheOldMountGambierGaol

- Backpacker favourite
- Vacation rental style
- Bed only options
- Kitchen facilities available

451

MIRAMIRA
FANTASY THEMED ACCOMMODATION

LOCATION AND ACTIVITIES

Located in beautiful Gippsland Region, just 90 minutes from Melbourne by car.

Visit local wineries & sample famous local cheeses, teamed with the winery's best at Wild Dog, Brandy Creek or Cannibal Creek to name just a few. Bush walking, fish for alpine trout at Noojee, take a tour of PowerWorks or visit the centennial rose garden at Morwell.

"Combining comfort and an indulgence with fantasy"

Bed and Breakfast properties don't have to be boring and at Mira Mira there is something for everyone.

Situated on 22 acres of bush land, Mira Mira is a collection of three self contained, two bedroom fantasy retreats where guests have an opportunity to 'Live in Art". On entering the Cave, Zen Retreat or Tanglewood retreats, the colours and beauty will take your breath away. Each has been designed to set your imagination wild and to capture the light, views and beauty of the natural environment around you. The perfect setting for relaxation, rejuvenation and romance.

MiraMiraAccommodation
Bloomfield Road
Crossover, Victoria
Australia
www.GoUnusual.com/MiraMiraAccommodation

HAPUKU LODGE
LUXURY TREEHOUSES

Conceived as a contemporary country inn, Hapuku Lodge has developed into one of New Zealand's most iconic luxury properties. Five Tree Houses were added to the modern lodge accommodation in 2006 ensuring the lodge has some of the most unusual luxury accommodation available in New Zealand. Throughout the lodge, the family owners have contributed their design skills, ensuring it fits within the spectacular environment. Custom designed and immaculately presented wooden furnishings inside, compliment the wooden cladding found around the lodge and Tree Houses.

LOCATION AND ACTIVITIES

The Tree Houses stand 10 metres off the ground amongst a stand of Manuka and Kanuka Trees. With large windows capping each end of these spacious rooms, one can look out to the snow-capped Kaikoura Mountains to the West and East across the Olive Grove to the Pacific Ocean. Inside, the Tree Houses are furnished with custom designed furnishings including ultra-comfortable beds and handcrafted wood, as well as all the amenities expected of a city-centre hotel including; large spa bath, wireless broadband, flat-panel TV, Ipod docking station, air conditioning, heated floors. The Tree Houses even have private fireplaces and small balconies.

"Tarzan and Jane never had it so good!"

Hapuku Lodge and Treehouses
Kaikoura, Canterbury
New Zealand
www.GoUnusual.com/HapukuLodgeandTreehouse

THE BOOT
GIANT BOOT

When Steve and partner Judy first created The Boot in 2001 they were considered slightly crazy, but after several years history of happy visitors they are rightly taking their place as local celebrities and contributing to the tapestry of attractions and folklore of this inspiring region.

Creating a giant boot guesthouse on a 6 acre property is perhaps the genius of an eccentric, and rather than convert an existing building, Steve Richards designed The Boot from scratch.

With curved walls and ceilings, everything had to be custom fitted into carefully planned spaces. The result is an unusual, romantic hideaway - in the shape of a giant boot!

Providing a queen-size double bed, facilities for hot drinks, a mini bar and bathroom with shower, kitchenette and courtyard barbecue for self catering. A continental or cooked breakfast is delivered from the nearby Jester House café to be enjoyed in the cosy bedroom, outside terrace or downstairs lounge. A supper platter can also be ordered for couples who relish the privacy and as many find when they arrive - that they really don't want to go out.

With a fireplace and under floor heating, The Boot is open year round, mainly to tourists in the summer months, but with steady bookings from knowledgeable locals keen for a relaxing break during the rest of the year.

LOCATION AND ACTIVITIES

Nearby Tasman is located between Nelson City and the Abel Tasman and Kahurangi National Parks at the top of the South Island of New Zealand. Around 35 mins drive from either Nelson airport, or Nelson harbour for ferry connections to North Island.

The nearby beaches of Kina and Ruby Bay offer beautiful, long relaxing walks, swimming or just lazing in the sun.

Next door to The Boot itself, the Jester House café has become a much loved coffee stop serving breakfast, lunch and inbetweens. The 6 acre estate also has a garden, enchanted forest and a tame eel attraction, offering feeding during summer months from September until May.

"Sleep in a giant boot!"

The Boot Bed'n'Breakfast
Jester House Estate, 320 Aporo Road
Tasman
New Zealand
www.GoUnusual.com/TheBootBednBreakfast

- Bed & Breakfast
- Restaurant nearby

WOODLYN PARK

STAY IN A TRAIN, PLANE, BOAT OR UNDERGROUND

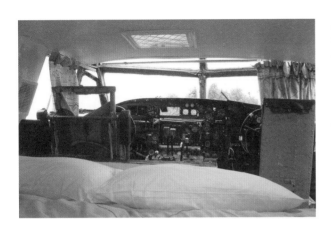

All the motels available at Woodlyn Park are self-contained with kitchens and own shower toilet facilities. They can accommodate between 2-10 people.

LOCATION AND ACTIVITIES

Woodlyn Park is between Auckland and Te Kuiti off the SH3. The park is about 5 minutes from the Waitomo Caves village tourist location.

"A choice of WOW to tell your friends about"

Woodlyn Park has four amazing World Unique Motel options:

A 1950's Bristol Freighter Plane fully refurbished into two beautiful self contained motel units. This plane was one of the last allied planes out of Vietnam and is the only accommodation of its type in the world.

"The Waitomo Express" - a 1918 Rail Carriage beautifully refurbished into a completely self contained motel unit having two separate bedrooms. The Waitomo Express sleeps eight people with one double bed, and two sets of single bunks.

Woodlyn Park also provides the Worlds First Hobbit Underground Motels with circular windows - straight out of middle earth!!!

Their latest vacation rental motel is a beached boat, with wooden bespoke interior - very nautical!

Woodlyn Park
1177 Waitomo Valley Rd
Waitomo Caves
Waikato
New Zealand
www.GoUnusual.com/WoodlynPark

- Self Catering motel
- Couples and Families
- Minimum stay in high season

459

ADDITIONAL PROPERTIES
AUSTRALIA

AUSTRALIA
Canopy Rainforest Treehouses and Wildlife Sanctuary
Tarzali, Queensland
Australia
5 timber pole houses in the heart of the ancient rainforest canopy
www.GoUnusual.com/TheCanopyRainforestTreehousesandWildlife-Sanctuary

Daintree Ecolodge
Daintree, Queensland
Australia
Offering award winning, unique tree house style resort
www.GoUnusual.com/DaintreeEcolodge

Desert Cave Hotel
Coober Pedy, South Australia
Australia
Underground hotel, casino and shops in Coober Pedy
www.GoUnusual.com/DesertCaveHotel

The Henry Jones Art Hotel
Hobart, TASMANIA
Australia
The former 1820 IXL Jam Factory - the flashiest factory you will ever sleep in
www.GoUnusual.com/TheHenryJonesArtHotel

Medina Grand Adelaide Treasury
Adelaide, South Australia
Australia
Historic 169-year-old colonial treasury
www.GoUnusual.com/MedinaGrandAdelaideTreasury

PJ's Underground Bed & Breakfast
Turley's Hill, White Cliffs, NSW
Australia
Hand built underground B+B with new rooms regularly added
www.GoUnusual.com/PJsUndergroundBedandBreakfast

Q Station Retreat
Manly, NSW
Australia
Peaceful retreat on the site of a former quarantine station
www.GoUnusual.com/QStationRetreat

St Killians - Hunter Valley, Near Brookfield:
Postal address: Narraweena, New South Wales
Australia
Nineteenth-century former church offers a very private getaway for couples
www.GoUnusual.com/StKillians-HunterValley

Thorngrove Manor
Adelaide, South Australia
Australia
Fairytale castle built from new for discrete rendezvous
www.GoUnusual.com/ThorngroveManor

The Underground Motel
White Cliffs, New South Wales
Australia
3 star AAA rated underground dwelling, pool and bar in New South Wales
www.GoUnusual.com/TheUndergroundMotel

"Well done is better than well said"

Henry Ford

"We live in a wonderful world that is full of beauty, charm and adventure. There is no end to the adventures we can have if only we seek them with our eyes open."

Jawaharial Nehru

Alphabetical Property Index

"A journey of a thousand miles

begins with a cash advance."

Alton Brown, Feasting on Asphalt: The River Run

Alphabetical Property Index

Alphabetical Property Index

"I shall be telling this with a sigh

somewhere ages and ages hence: Two

roads diverged in a wood, and I – I took

the one less traveled by, and that has

made all the difference."

Robert Frost

How we chose entries for this book

Properties do not pay to be listed in this printed guide. All are members of the gounusual.com online community and UnusualHotelsOfTheWorld.com website, chosen by editors around the world. With an average of a million unique visitors every year, the online guide is viewed by someone searching for inspiration every 20 seconds, 24 hours a day, 365 days a year.

The most popular get top ranked for selection to this printed guide. Those that don't make the editorial criteria for "having a story" won't get listed at all...

On a regular basis we review ratings for the most fantastic of our properties to create a WOW list of team favourites, posted online. Our recent New entries and Top Picks are also highlighted.

How do we make money?
Online community properties pay annual fees to access the tens of thousands of direct contact requests and inquiries generated.
Properties also benefit from the global publicity that UHOTW.com and GoUnusual.com membership generates.

Good news for Properties
Annual fees paid by properties give them syndicated access to a global community of thousands of journalists, reviewers, editors and researchers for print, TV, radio and online media that they'd be unable to afford to reach on their own. Of course, properties listed get access to hundreds of thousands of visitors interested to travel, and their requests to get in contact too!

Good news for Travellers
Online guide visitors are put in contact with the properties direct - so no middlemen taking a fee - and special deals for GoUnusual generated inquiries.

Find out more online at www.GoUnusual.com

CONTRIBUTORS AND REGIONAL EDITORS

This guide wouldn't be possible without the kind support of the global team of Unusual Hotels of the World contributors and regional editors:

Andrea Nims, Carl Hildebrand, Daniel Gibney, EriCK Prillwitz, Mustafa Gorgun, Pradeep and Rashmi Mansukhani, Sharla Ault, Stefan Schneider, Vince Ross, Vivienne Willison, Water Baby.

Plus of course friends including: Alex Mountain, Andrea Rademan, Caroline Pearson, Charlotte Lozier, Chris Lahey, Colin Dutton, Doug Grant, Esteban Zarate, Emma Willingale, Geraldine Pucken, Holly Smales, Joanne Patterson, Greg Pantaine, Marco Scurati, Mike Dingle, Mitzy Applegate, Nikki Penn-Jones, Ray Mason, Richard Clarke, Sam Stoyan, Simon Roberts, Timo Kiippa.

Thank you to Sharla Ault for her editorial assistance, writing and inspiration. Thank you to the Landmark Trust, Belgian Tourist Board, and Sud de France Développment for supporting UHOTW with text and photography. Thank you to EriCK Prillwitz and Sam Styles for their photos.

A big thank you to the property owners, managers and photographers for their contributions, support and encouragement.

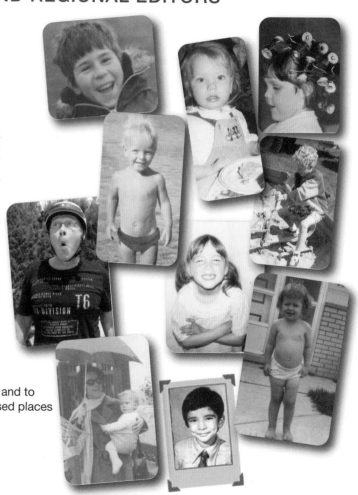

We are always looking for new friends to suggest properties and to champion our message to "sleep with a story". If we've missed places or you want to join our team, contact us at
The Unusual Company Limited
PO Box 298
CHERTSEY, Surrey KT16 6DT
United Kingdom
or email online to info@gounusual.com

ACKNOWLEDGEMENTS

With love as always to my two favourite reviewers, Arran and Oliver.

To Geoff Dobson, Claire, Alice and Yvette, Mum and Dad - with lots of Love. Russ and KB Strawson, Dan, June and Jack Stride, Mike, Lynette, William and Henry Edwards, Karen and Gavin Carr, Jay and Anna, for being there and never quitting when things were tough. Caroline D'Subin for the happiness we shared. RIP Leni. Simon Penn, Sid Lalwani, Laxmi, Kayin and Zoe - without whom I'd never have started. Pankaj Malav and the team at Iniquus - for your patience and tech savvy. Trevor and Jane Mewse, Katharine and Jon Hulls for smiles and happiness, afloat and ashore. Thank you Princess for inspiration taking care of Ben. Merci as always to Thomas and everyone at Jonglez publishing. Sue Whitfield, Steve, Naimh, Annie and Joshua Dyer- my biggest fans and great friends. Mark Williams, Lisa and Hayden Littlewood for helping me stay sane when everything came crashing down. Tom, Lynne, Tommy and William Stone, Debbie, Martin, Alex and Euan Astley - thank you always. Phil and Carol, Jaz, Marcia, Neve and Tia Francis; Dave, Alison and the Harris family; Matt, Clare and the Wells clan - smiles and hugs to Bristol. Vivien Russell for services beyond the call of flight crew. Heather White networking with a smile. Ruth, Pete and the Wailes family. Lynn Forbes, norty lady! Hola Heather, Stuart, Sonny and Lois Burrell, wishing you were next door again. Françoise Scheepers - merci de votre confiance. Thank you Aurélien Defaye and the team at Sud de France Développment and Maison de Languedoc Roussillon. Thank you Daniel Gibney for keeping online alive this year. Kate and Stuart Gulliver, Nick Bullett, Steve Griffiths, Myles (and Emma), Jon, Mark, Gary (and Lucy), Derek (and Jane), fellow Grifters members, friends and coaches at Weybridge Vandals RFC - for mud, beer, tea and bacon sandwiches on Sunday morning. Hello again to Pam and Brian Bliss, with memories of Paris and Martini's too long ago. My friends at Coxes Lock, Jo, Paul and Eulyn, Matt & Andy, Gemma & Tom, Mark Spence, Liz and Jon, Toby Hockin and SteveM, Mike and Kate Gerrard - thank you for Gin'n'Tonic, tea and checking that I am still breathing. For those I've forgotten - sorry. Get in contact more often!

Finally, thank you to Noelle Murphy and Ashling Mosley for lots of smiles.

THANK YOU

ALL photographs are reproduced with kind permission of the following;
©PixelHotel, Schneedorf Igloo Village-©Hans Lebiedzik, The Proposal - © Benjamin Hofer, Baumhaus Hotel - © www.kulturinsel.com, Blow Up Hall 5050 - © Nelec Studio photography, Karostas Cietums - ©Paul Kubisztal, The Atomium www.atomium.be SABAM 2010, La Balade des Gnomes - ©Noel, ©BeManos, ©Hotel Bloom!, La Classe, Les Duves – ©Jean-Luc Laloux, ©EuroSpace Centre, ThePantoneHotel™ – ©Sven Laurent, ©QuartierLatin, ©Hotel Welcome, Krumlov Tower-©JiriMudrych, HôtelParticulierMontmartre – ©Morgane Rosseau, ©UnCoinChezSoi, Château du Pé © Bernard Renoux, Villa Chiminée - © T. Nishi, PropellerIslandCityLodge–©Lars Stroschen, ©AbaliGranSultanato, ©Ca Maria Adele, ©CasaBrennaTosatto, CastelloDiPetroia-©Sagrini, LaurinSuite-©Laurin, ©LocandaRosaRosae, Maison Moschino ©MassimoListri /MartinaBarberini /AkeE:sonLindman, ©MasseriaCervarolo, ©MasseriaMontenapoleone, ©MetropoleHotel, PalazzoBarbarigo–©HotelPhilosophy, ©HotelParchiDelGarda, ColorHotel - ©Crimapi Hotels srl, Follonico–Sibilia Style and Resorts srl, Hotel Greif – ©Annette_Fischer, Relais Cattedrale - © italian notes, GLAMPING Canonici - © Stefano Scatà, Siena House – ©Malvin Tyler, ©SanLorenzo MountainLodge, Torre Prendiparte – ©MGiovanardi, ©VIVERE, AirplaneSuite - ©Hotelsuites.nl, Zeelandmolen - © Peter Verkerk, CapsuleHotel - ©Denis Oudendijk, CraneHotel - ©Dromen aan Zee, Controversy Tram Hotel – ©Frank&Irma Appel / ©uhotw.com, ©VerbekeFoundation, Hotel Brosundet, Hotel Union Øye, Molja Lighthouse, Storfjord Hotel, Svinoey Lighthouse – ©Steve Michael Røyset/62NORD AS, Juvet – ©Studio Per Eide, Malhadinha Nova Vineyard & Spa – ©Herdade da Malhadinha Nova, ©Muxima, ©NespereiraEstate, ©Hotel EntrenteArte, ©Cabanas als Arbres, Hotel Puerta America - ©HotelSilken (Madrid) Photo Rafael Vargas, ©RefugioMarnesCasasRurales, Ushuaïa Ibiza Beach Hotel - ©FiestaHotelGroup, Jumbo Stay - ©Oscar Diös, Kolarbyn–©Lars Gabrielsson / ©Skogens_Konung / ©Mikaela Larm, Sala Silvermine–©Pappilabild, Utter Inn - Mikael Genberg© Västerås & Co, WoodpeckerHotel – Mikael Genberg © Västerås & Co/©uhotw.com, TREEHOTEL Interior: © Peter Lundstrom, WDO, Exterior: © Kent Lindvall Treehotel, ICEHOTEL - ©Marcus Dillistone / ©Natalia Chistyakova & Karlis Ile, Iglu-Dorf Engelberg – ©perretfoto.ch, ©Jailhotel.ch, La Claustra - ©BAREST AG, ©Cappadocia Cave Resort & Spa, ©TheMarmaraAntalya, ©MuseumHotel, Fort Clonque, Nicolle Tower, Beckford's Tower, The Egypian House, Lundy, Luttrell's Tower, Hampton Court Palace, Appleton Water Tower, Martello Tower, The House of Correction, Gothic Temple, Freston Tower, Beamsley Hospital, Culloden Tower, the Music Room, The Pineapple - ©The Landmark Trust, Additional Hampton Court Palace shots -

©Sam Styles, Beach Sun Retreat - ©KEmanuelsson, The Chocolate Boutique Hotel – ©Paul Underhill, Crazy Bear Beaconsfield & Oxford – ©CrazyBearGroup, Enchanted Manor - © Chris Cowley, ©PavilionLondon, ©Railholiday, ©Vintage Vacations, AuroraExpress ©KaitlinWilson, Dog Bark Park - © DogBarkPark, El Cosmico - © Nick Simonite, ©Jules Undersea Lodge, ©FreeSpiritSpheres, ©FeatherbedRailroad, ©Saugerties, Wigwam Motel California – ©Manoj Patel, ©Winvian, ©Casa Margot Hotel Champagnerie, Palacio de Sal – ©EriCK Prillwitz, Elqui Domos – ©EstebanZarate, ©Hotel Antumalal, ©Magic Mountain Hotel – ©Lodge Montaña Mágica, ©MajahuitasResort, ©VERANA, ©XinalaniRetreat, Canopy Tower Ecolodge and Nature Observatory - ©David Tipling/CanopyTower Photo: RadP, ©Elsewhere, HippoPointWildlifeSanctuaryTower - ©HippoPoint (Management Ltd.), ©TheOld MountGambierGaol, The Boot Bed'n'Breakfast – ©HarrietteRichards, ©HapukuLodge, ©Woodlyn Park, Kasbah du Toubkal – ©DiscoverLtd/©Alan Keohane, Hatari Lodge & Shu'mata camp – ©TheAfricanEmbassy/©Martin Mueller, DasParkHotel, Manoir de Lébioles, ICEHOTEL, ©uhotw.com,

Other shots used with kind permission.

Design and Layout: **PDA Design**
© The Unusual Company 2013
ISBN: 978-0-9565981-1-0
Printed in the UK

We would like to dedicate this book to our beautiful friend Anne (Pixiepants) Gray.

We met her many years ago at Weybridge Vandals Rugby Club and she is a very special lady. Not only has she been amazingly courageous in her fight against breast cancer, but she has continued to raise money for the local hospice and inspire many people along the way.........**we all love you Anne xxxx**

The Gullies, Bulletts, Reeds, Bryants, Hollings' and Mellows'

**WEYBRIDGE
VANDALS R.F.C**

"Adventure is worthwhile."

Aristotle

STEVE DOBSON LOVES new experiences and tries to enjoy the journey as much as the destination. Lost bags, pointless delays, cancellations and last-minute diversions have made some trips unnecessarily challenging - but memorable nevertheless. Whatever the situation he tries to keep his sense of humour in the search for the silver lining in the latest cloud.

Setting up UnusualHotelsOfTheWorld.com and GoUnusual.com with friends Simon Penn and Sid Lalwani in 2004 to catalogue memorable places to stay, they have built a fun-loving team of travel contributors. All are keen to share their notes of the most interesting and unusual places to stay around the world. On their many adventures the trio have argued, shouted and questioned their own sanity on several occasions, but thankfully remain the best of friends.

Steve is 45, and lives in a mill in Surrey with his 2 children. He travels when childcare allows, or whenever he can take the kids.

This is his fourth title. He hopes you enjoy it!

By the same author,
Unusual Hotels of the World

Unusual Hotels of the UK
and Ireland

Unusual Hotels of Europe -
Jonglez Publishing

The Unusual Company Ltd. PO Box 298 CHERTSEY Surrey KT16 6DT Company registration GB 5107362

The Unusual Company Ltd. manages a number of guide, trip and media activities including the UnusualHotelsOfTheWorld.com and GoUnusual.com websites. If you've suggestions of properties we've missed, please email us at info@gounusual.com.

By the same author,
Unusual Hotels of the World - Jonglez Publishing
Unusual Hotels of the UK and Ireland - Jonglez Publishing
Unusual Hotels Europe - Jonglez Publishing

ISBN 978-0-9565981-1-0
Thank you for your interest in the small print. Happy Travels!

Graphics and Typesetting by PDA Design and Print. Printed in the UK.

A CIP catalogue record for this book is available from the British Library.

ISBN: 978-0-9565981-1-0

9 780956 598110

£15.99 / €20,00 / US$25.00
ISBN 978-0-9565981-1-0